THE BOOK OF

AFTERNOON
Tea

THE BOOK OF

AFTERNOON
Tea

LESLEY MACKLEY

Photographed by
JON STEWART

a Salamander book

Published by Salamander Books Limited
LONDON • NEW YORK

Published 1992 by Salamander Books Limited
129-137 York Way, London N7 9LG, United Kingdom

© Salamander Books Ltd 1992

ISBN 0 86101 724 2

Distributed by Hodder & Stoughton Services, PO Box 6,
Mill Road, Dunton Green, Sevenoaks, Kent TN13 2XX

Managing Editor: Felicity Jackson
Art Director: Roger Daniels
Editor: Louise Steele
Photographer: Jon Stewart, assisted by Sandra Lambell
Home Economist: Sandra Baddeley
Typeset by: BMD Graphics, Hemel Hempstead
Colour separation by: Scantrans Pte. Ltd, Singapore
Printed in Belgium by Proost International Book Production

ACKNOWLEDGEMENTS

The Publishers would like to thank the following for their
help and advice:
Barbara Stewart at Prop Exchange, Unit F,
51 Calthorpe Street, London WC1.

Companion volumes of interest:

The Book of SOUPS
The Book of COCKTAILS
The Book of CHOCOLATES & PETITS FOURS
The Book of HORS D'OEUVRES
The Book of GARNISHES
The Book of BREAKFASTS & BRUNCHES
The Book of PRESERVES
The Book of SAUCES
The Book of DESSERTS
The Book of ICE CREAMS & SORBETS
The Book of GIFTS FROM THE PANTRY
The Book of PASTA
The Book of HOT & SPICY NIBBLES-DIPS-DISHES
The Book of CRÊPES & OMELETTES
The Book of FONDUES
The Book of CHRISTMAS FOODS
The Book of BISCUITS
The Book of CHEESECAKES
The Book of CURRIES & INDIAN FOODS
The Book of PIZZAS & ITALIAN BREADS
The Book of SANDWICHES
The Book of SALADS
The Book of GRILLING & BARBECUES
The Book of DRESSINGS & MARINADES
The Book of CHINESE COOKING
The Book of CAKE DECORATING
The Book of MEXICAN FOODS
The Book of ANTIPASTI
The Book of THAI COOKING
The Book of CHILDREN'S FOODS

Notes:
All spoon measurements are equal.
1 teaspoon = 5 ml spoon
1 tablespoon = 15 ml spoon.

CONTENTS

INTRODUCTION

As various food fads come and go, many people now long to return to a more traditional and leisurely style of eating, and in an age when everyone is constantly busy and rushing, what could be more enjoyable than to take time to indulge in what was once part of everyday life, but has now become a luxury — afternoon tea.

Afternoon tea is a perfect way of entertaining just a few friends or a large crowd, and can be anything from an intimate gathering around a roaring fire on a winter afternoon, to a relaxed party in the garden on a sunny summer day.

With over 100 recipes (all with helpful step-by-step photographs), *The Book of Afternoon Tea* has recipes for every occasion. Some are traditional favourites, guaranteed to bring back nostalgic memories, and alongside them are recipes which our Victorian and Edwardian ancestors certainly would not recognise, but which are welcome additions to any tea table.

So look out your prettiest tablecloth and best china and indulge your family and friends in a delightful treat.

AFTERNOON TEA

The custom of taking afternoon tea is thought to have been introduced in England in 1840 by Anna, the seventh Duchess of Bedford. At that time, lunch was taken early and dinner was not served in the evening until about 9 o'clock. Not surprisingly, the Duchess became rather hungry during the course of the afternoon and began to ask for some tea, bread and butter and cake to be brought to her room. This quickly became a habit and she started asking friends to join her.

It was soon fashionable to take tea in the middle of the afternoon and the occasion became increasingly elaborate with elegant teaware available in the form of lace tablecloths and bone china tea services, and the ladies would change into long tea gowns in which they would preside over ornate silver teapots while engaging in general, lightweight conversation.

In Edwardian times tea shops began to flourish and tea rooms in department stores became popular. Smart hotels providing elaborate and elegant afternoon teas were fashionable meeting places.

A TRADITIONAL AFTERNOON TEA

Afternoon tea has lost favour since the Second World War; life is lived at a faster pace, often making it impractical to stop in the middle of the afternoon for a leisurely tea. However, it is a habit well worth reviving, even if only for an occasional moment of self indulgence. Afternoon tea should be a graceful event; an opportunity to display the best china and table linen, and a time for people of all ages to gather together for relaxation and refreshment.

The choice of food served for afternoon tea depends on the occasion, the time of year and personal taste, but a traditional tea consists of a selection of sandwiches and savouries followed by scones and preserves, pastries, biscuits, plain cake and tea breads with a more elaborate cake as a centrepiece. At a winter's fireside tea, toast and crumpets or muffins would be served with butter and savoury or sweet spreads.

The essential drink to accompany afternoon tea is, of course, tea, but many other drinks are also traditionally served, depending on the time of year. In the summer iced tea, fruit cordials and light fruit cups are very refreshing, and in the winter, spiced tea or warming punches are always popular.

The type of tea to serve is a matter of personal taste, but it is a good idea to offer a choice of Indian or China tea, or a fragrant Earl Grey or Lapsang Souchong. Herbal or fruit teas are also becoming increasingly poular. China and other delicately flavoured teas should be served with slices of lemon rather than milk.

MAKING TEA
It is worth taking trouble to produce a good cup of tea.
- Use good quality tea.
- Fill the kettle from the cold tap.
- Warm the teapot.
- Use 1 teaspoon of tea for every 175 ml (6 fl oz/¾ cup) water.
- When the water is boiling, pour it onto the tea, replace the lid and leave to infuse for 3-5 minutes.
- Serve tea freshly made. If possible, put the tea leaves in an infuser, so that they can be removed when the tea is the desired strength.

—CUCUMBER & DILL HEARTS—

¼ cucumber
½ teaspoon wine vinegar
½ teaspoon salt
45 g (1½ oz/9 teaspoons butter), softened
4 slices white bread
pepper
1 teaspoon chopped fresh dill
TO GARNISH:
dill sprigs

Peel cucumber and slice into paper thin slices. Place in a colander and sprinkle with the vinegar and salt. Leave for 30 minutes.

Pat cucumber slices dry on absorbent kitchen paper. Butter the bread. Arrange cucumber slices over 2 slices buttered bread. Season with pepper and scatter chopped dill over the top. Cover with remaining bread slices and press together.

Using a heart-shaped cutter, cut 4 heart shapes from each sandwich. Arrange on a serving plate and garnish with sprigs of dill.

Makes 8.

EGG & CRESS CIRCLES

4 eggs
4 tablespoons mayonnaise
1 teaspoon Dijon mustard
2 teaspoons Worcestershire sauce
few drops Tabasco
salt and pepper
85 g (3 oz/⅓ cup) butter, softened
8 large slices white bread
bunch mustard and cress
TO GARNISH:
mustard and cress

Bring a pan of water to the boil. Carefully put in eggs, bring back to the boil. Boil for 10-12 minutes.

Drain eggs, crack shells lightly and leave in a bowl of cold water until completely cold. Remove shells and roughly chop eggs with a knife. Add mayonnaise, mustard, Worcestershire sauce, Tabasco and salt and pepper. Mix well together.

Butter bread. Spread egg mixture on 4 slices of buttered bread. Scatter mustard and cress over egg. Cover with remaining bread slices and press together. Cut off crusts from bread. Using a 5 cm (2 in) round cutter, cut 4 circles from each sandwich. Arrange on a serving plate and garnish with mustard and cress.

Makes 16.

ITALIAN TEMPTERS

4 large slices white bread
45 g (1½ oz/9 teaspoons) butter, softened
4 teaspoons ready-made pesto
4 tomatoes
salt and pepper
115 g (4 oz) Mozzarella cheese
TO GARNISH:
fresh basil leaves

Spread slices of bread with butter. Using a 5 cm (2 in) round cutter, cut 4 rounds from each slice.

Spread a little pesto over each circle. Cut the ends off each tomato and slice each tomato into 4. Place a slice on each bread round. Season with salt and pepper.

Cut Mozarella into cubes. Arrange cubes on tomato slices. Arrange on a serving dish, garnished with fresh basil leaves.

Makes 16.

Note: Ready-made pesto is available in larger supermarkets and specialist food shops.

──── STRIPED SANDWICHES ────

85 g (3 oz) sliced ham
4 teaspoons mayonnaise
½ teaspoon Dijon mustard
55 g (2 oz/¼ cup) cream cheese
4 teaspoons chopped fresh chives
salt and pepper
130 g (4½ oz/½ cup plus 3 teaspoons) butter, softened
2 slices white bread
2 slices wholemeal bread
TO GARNISH:
fresh chives

Chop ham finely. Put in a bowl with mayonnaise and mustard. Mix well together.

In a bowl, mix together cream cheese, chives and salt and pepper. Butter 2 slices white and brown bread on one side only and the remaining 2 slices white and brown bread on both sides.

Spread half the ham mixture over 2 slices of brown bread. Cover with white bread which has been buttered on both sides. Spread cream cheese mixture over white bread. Cover with the brown bread which has been buttered on both sides, spread over remaining ham and top with the white bread. Remove crusts from bread. Cut each sandwich into 6 slices. Arrange on a serving plate and garnish with fresh chives.

Makes 12.

— PASTRAMI SANDWICHES —

15 g (½ oz) watercress
55 g (2 oz) pastrami
55 g (2 oz/¼ cup) cottage cheese
2 teaspoons mayonnaise
salt and pepper
45 g (1½ oz/9 teaspoons) butter
4 slices light rye bread
TO GARNISH:
watercress sprigs

Chop the watercress finely and chop the pastrami quite finely.

In a bowl, mix together watercress, pastrami, cottage cheese and mayonnaise and season to taste with salt and pepper.

Butter slices of bread. Spread pastrami mixture over 2 bread slices. Cover with remaining bread slices and press down. Cut off crusts from bread. Cut each sandwich into 4 triangles. Arrange on a serving plate and garnish with watercress.

Makes 8.

AVOCADO & BACON SANDWICHES

115 g (4 oz) bacon rashers
1 ripe avocado
½ teaspoon lemon juice
salt and pepper
45 g (1½ oz/9 teaspoons) butter, softened
4 large slices wholemeal bread
TO GARNISH:
lemon twist and parsley sprig

Remove rind from bacon. Chop bacon roughly and put into a frying pan. Heat gently until fat begins to run, then fry until bacon is crisp. Drain on absorbent kitchen paper.

Peel avocado, taking care not to remove bright green flesh just inside skin. Cut in half and remove stone. In a bowl, mash avocado, stir in lemon juice and salt and pepper.

Butter bread. Spread avocado mixture on 2 bread slices. Scatter bacon over avocado. Cover with remaining bread slices and press together. Cut off crusts from bread. Cut each sandwich into 4 triangles. Arrange on a serving plate, garnished with a lemon twist and parsley sprig.

Makes 8.

– SPICY CHICKEN SANDWICHES –

115 g (4 oz) cooked chicken
2 teaspoons mango chutney
8 teaspoons mayonnaise
½ teaspoon curry powder
1 teaspoon lime juice
salt
45 g (1 ½ oz/9 teaspoons) butter, softened
4 slices granary bread
TO GARNISH:
lime twist and dill sprig

Chop the cooked chicken into small pieces and set aside.

If there are any large pieces of fruit in the chutney, chop them finely. Put chutney in a bowl with mayonnaise, curry powder, lime juice and salt. Mix well together. Stir in chopped chicken.

Butter bread. Divide chicken mixture between 2 slices of bread. Cover with remaining bread slices and press well together. Cut off crusts from bread. Cut each sandwich into 4 squares. Arrange on a serving plate, garnished with a lime twist and a dill sprig.

Makes 8.

TURKEY TRIANGLES

45 g (1 ½ oz/9 teaspoons) butter
4 slices white bread
4 crisp lettuce leaves
85 g (3 oz) turkey, sliced thinly
salt and pepper
4 teaspoons cranberry sauce
TO GARNISH:
cocktail gherkins, cut into fan shapes

Butter the bread. Arrange the lettuce leaves over 2 of the bread slices.

Arrange sliced turkey over lettuce. Season with salt and pepper. Spread cranberry sauce over remaining bread slices and place cranberry side down over turkey slices. Press together.

Cut off crusts from bread. Cut each sandwich into 4 triangles. Arrange on a serving plate, garnished with cocktail gherkins.

Makes 8.

Variation: Cranberry jelly may be used instead of cranberry sauce, if wished.

PRAWN FINGERS

115 ml (4 fl oz/½ cup) double (thick) cream
1 teaspoon tomato purée (paste)
1 teaspoon lemon juice
few drops Tabasco sauce
salt
115 g (4 oz) peeled cooked prawns, thawed if frozen
4 small finger rolls
55 g (2 oz/¼ cup) butter
cayenne pepper
TO GARNISH:
cucumber slices, prawns and mint sprigs

In a bowl, whip cream until thick enough to
hold soft peaks.

Add tomato purée (paste), lemon juice,
Tabasco sauce and salt. Mix together gently.
Pat prawns dry with absorbent kitchen paper
and add to cream mixture.

Cut rolls in half lengthways and butter each
half. Spread prawn mixture on the bottom
half of each buttered roll. Arrange on a
serving plate. Sprinkle with cayenne pepper
and replace top. Garnish with cucumber
slices, prawns and mint sprigs.

Makes 4.

──────SALMON PINWHEELS──────

1 large unsliced sandwich loaf
55 g (2 oz/¼ cup) butter, softened
55 g (2 oz) watercress
115 g (4 oz) thinly sliced smoked salmon
pepper
1 teaspoon lemon juice
TO GARNISH:
watercress

Cut crusts from loaf of bread. Cut two 0.5 cm
(¼ in) thick lengthways slices from loaf.
Using a rolling pin, roll each slice of bread
firmly to flatten.

Spread butter over slices of bread. Remove
stalks from watercress and arrange the leaves
over the bread. Arrange slices of smoked
salmon over the watercress. Season with
pepper and sprinkle with lemon juice.

Roll up each slice, like a Swiss roll, starting
from a short side. Wrap rolls tightly in plastic
wrap and chill for at least 2 hours. Remove
plastic wrap and cut each roll into 7 pinwheels. Arrange on a serving plate, garnished
with watercress.

Makes 14.

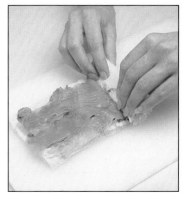

— STILTON & PEAR POCKETS —

4 pitta breads
2 ripe pears
55 g (2 oz) Stilton cheese
55 g (2 oz/½ cup) chopped walnuts
TO GARNISH:
lettuce leaves

Grill pitta breads lightly so that they puff up. Cut each pitta bread in half through the centre. Open each half to make a pocket.

Peel pears, remove cores and chop flesh coarsely. Put in a bowl with the crumbled Stilton cheese. Add chopped walnuts and mix together.

Divide pear mixture between pitta pockets. Arrange on a serving plate, garnished with lettuce leaves. Serve at once.

Makes 8.

–DATE & WALNUT SANDWICHES–

85 g (3 oz/½ cup) dates
25 g (1 oz/⅓ cup) walnuts
45 g (1½ oz/9 teaspoons) cream cheese
4 large slices or 8 small slices fruit bread
3 teaspoons thick honey
pinch cinnamon
TO DECORATE:
a few dates and walnuts

Chop dates quite finely. Chop walnuts finely.

Spread cream cheese onto all the bread slices. Spread honey over half the slices on top of the cheese. Scatter dates and walnuts over the honey-coated slices and sprinkle with cinnamon.

Cover with remaining bread slices and press together. Cut off crusts from bread. Cut large sandwiches into 4 squares or small ones in half. Arrange on a serving plate, decorated with dates and walnuts.

Makes 8.

Variation: White or wholemeal bread may be used instead of fruit bread.

SALAMI PUFFS

175 g (6 oz) puff pastry
8 slices Italian salami
25 g (1 oz/¼ cup) grated Cheddar cheese
beaten egg, to glaze
TO GARNISH:
lamb's lettuce or parsley sprigs

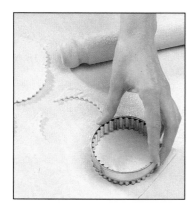

Preheat oven to 200C (400F/Gas 6). On a floured surface, roll out pastry 0.3 cm (⅛ in) thick. Using a 10 cm (4 in) fluted cutter, cut out 8 circles of pastry.

Lay a slice of salami in the middle of each pastry circle. Put a little cheese on each slice of salami.

In a bowl, beat egg and brush around edges of pastry. Fold pastry circle in half and press edges firmly to seal. Brush each puff with beaten egg. Bake in the oven for 15 minutes until well risen and golden brown. Serve garnished with lamb's lettuce or parsley.

Makes 8.

——DEVILLED HAM TOASTS——

115 g (4 oz) lean ham
3 teaspoons Worcestershire sauce
cayenne pepper, to taste
2 teaspoons French mustard
6 slices bread
55 g (2 oz/¼ cup) butter
TO GARNISH:
3 stuffed olives, sliced
watercress sprigs

Chop ham very finely, or mince. In a bowl, mix together ham, Worcestershire sauce, cayenne pepper and mustard.

Toast bread. Using a 5 cm (2 in) plain cutter, cut 2 circles from each slice of bread. Butter each circle of toast using 30 g (1 oz/ 6 teaspoons) of the butter and keep warm. In a saucepan, melt remaining butter. Add ham mixture. Cook, stirring, over a low heat until mixture is hot.

Spread ham mixture over toast circles. Garnish with stuffed olives and arrange on a serving plate with watercress sprigs. Serve at once.

Makes 12.

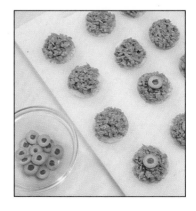

POTTED PRAWNS

350 g (12 oz) peeled small prawns
salt
cayenne pepper, to taste
1 teaspoon lemon juice
1/2 teaspoon ground ginger
175 g (6 oz/3/4 cup) butter
3 teaspoons finely chopped fresh chives
TO GARNISH:
chives and lemon slices (optional)
TO SERVE:
French bread or buttered toast

If using thawed frozen prawns, pat dry with absorbent kitchen paper.

Put prawns in a bowl with salt, cayenne pepper, lemon juice and ground ginger. Set aside in a cool place. In a saucepan, melt butter over a very low heat. Pour the clear liquid into a bowl, leaving the milky residue in the pan. Stir in chopped chives. Leave to stand for 20 minutes.

Divide prawns between 6 small ramekin dishes. Spoon chive butter over, pressing prawns down until covered with butter. Chill until firm. Garnish with chives and lemon slices, if wished, and serve with French bread or toast.

Serves 6.

—CRAB & GINGER TRIANGLES—

200 g (7 oz) can crabmeat, drained
6 spring onions, finely chopped
2.5 cm (1 in) piece fresh root ginger, peeled and grated
2 teaspoons soy sauce
salt and pepper
6 large sheets filo pastry about 35 cm (14 in) square
85 g (3 oz/⅓ cup) butter, melted
TO GARNISH:
spring onion slivers or tassels

In a bowl, mix together crabmeat, spring onions, ginger, soy sauce and salt and pepper. Set aside.

Preheat oven to 180C (350F/Gas 4). Lightly grease a baking sheet. Work with 1 sheet of pastry at a time, keeping the rest covered with a damp cloth. Cut sheet of pastry in half. Brush each half with melted butter and fold in half lengthways. Brush pastry all over with melted butter. Put a portion of crab mixture in 1 corner of 1 strip of pastry. Fold pastry and filling over at right angles to make a triangle and continue folding in this way along strip of pastry to make a triangular parcel.

Repeat with remaining pastry and crab mixture. Brush each parcel with melted butter. Bake in the oven for 20-25 minutes until crisp and golden brown. Serve warm, garnished with spring onion slivers or tassels.

Makes 12.

TUNA TOASTIES

200 g (7 oz) can tuna fish
3 tomatoes
85 g (3 oz) Cheddar cheese
4 slices bread
25 g (1 oz/6 teaspoons) butter
TO GARNISH:
dill sprigs

Preheat oven to 200C (400F/Gas 6). Drain tuna fish, put into a bowl and flake. Slice tomatoes. Grate cheese.

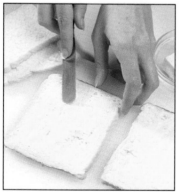

Spread one side of each slice of bread with butter. Place bread slices buttered sides down on a baking sheet.

Spread tuna fish over bread. Arrange tomatoes on top and cover with grated cheese. Bake in the oven for 8-10 minutes until bubbling. Cool for 1 minute, then cut each slice across into 2 triangles. Serve hot, garnished with dill.

Makes 8.

— SMOKED SALMON CROÛTES —

150 ml (5 fl oz/⅔ cup) thick sour cream
55 g (2 oz/¼ cup) butter
3 teaspoons sunflower oil
eight 2 cm (¾ in) thick slices of round-shaped bread
115 g (4 oz) smoked salmon
TO GARNISH:
dill sprigs

In a bowl, whisk sour cream until thick and smooth. Set aside. In a frying pan, heat butter and oil and fry bread, in batches, on both sides until golden. Drain on absorbent kitchen paper and keep warm.

Cut smoked salmon into strips about 13 x 2 cm (5 x ¾ in) and roll each one up loosely.

Place 4 rolls of smoked salmon on each croûte. Spoon a little of the sour cream over salmon. Garnish each croûte with a sprig of dill.

Makes 8.

PARMESAN BEIGNETS

55 g (2 oz/¼ cup) butter
70 g (2½ oz/½ cup plus 6 teaspoons) plain flour, sifted
2 eggs, beaten
1 teaspoon chopped fresh parsley
55 g (2 oz/½ cup) Parmesan cheese, grated
25 g (1 oz/¼ cup) grated Cheddar cheese
salt and pepper
oil for deep frying
TO GARNISH:
parsley sprigs

In a large pan, melt butter, add 150 ml (5 fl oz/⅔ cup) water and bring to the boil.

Add flour, all at once, and beat thoroughly until mixture leaves the side of the pan. Cool slightly, then vigorously beat in eggs, a little at a time. Stir in parsley, cheeses and salt and pepper to taste. Continue beating until cheese has melted.

One-third fill a deep fat fryer with vegetable oil and heat to 182C/360F. Carefully drop 4 or 5 walnut-sized spoonfuls of mixture into hot oil. Deep fry for 2-3 minutes until puffed and golden brown. Drain on absorbent kitchen paper and keep warm until all the beignets are fried. Serve garnished with parsley sprigs.

Makes about 16.

—— WELSH RAREBIT FINGERS ——

225 g (8 oz) mature Cheddar cheese
25 g (1 oz/6 teaspoons) butter
3 teaspoons Worcestershire sauce
1 teaspoon mustard powder
3 teaspoons plain flour
55 ml (2 fl oz/¼ cup) beer
4 slices wholemeal bread
TO GARNISH:
cayenne pepper for dusting
strips of red pepper (capsicum)
parsley sprigs

Grate cheese into a bowl. Add butter, Worcestershire sauce, mustard, flour and sufficient beer to make a stiff paste.

Toast bread on both sides. Spread cheese mixture over one side of each slice of toast.

Grill gently until topping is cooked through and well browned. Dust with cayenne pepper. Cut each slice of toast into 3 fingers. Garnish with strips of red pepper (capsicum) and parsley sprigs.

Makes 12.

MINI QUICHES

1½ quantities Shortcrust Pastry, see page 89
3 egg yolks
1 egg
salt and pepper, to taste
300 ml (10 fl oz/1¼ cups) whipping cream
MUSHROOM FILLING:
15 g (½ oz/3 teaspoons) butter
115 g (4 oz) mushrooms, finely chopped
PEPPER FILLING:
15 g (½ oz/3 teaspoons) butter
1 red pepper (capsicum), seeded and chopped

Preheat oven to 200C (400F/Gas 6). Grease 12 individual 6 cm (2½ in) flan tins.

To make mushroom filling, melt butter in a small pan. Add mushrooms and cook gently until soft and liquid has evaporated. Set aside. To make pepper filling, melt remaining butter in another small pan. Add the pepper (capsicum) and cook gently until beginning to soften. Set aside. On a floured surface, roll out pastry to 0.3cm (⅛ in) thick. Use to line prepared tins; prick bases with a fork.

Press a square of foil into each one; bake blind for 15 minutes, removing foil after 12 minutes. In a bowl, beat together egg yolks, egg, salt and pepper and cream. Put half the mixture in a bowl with the mushrooms and half in a bowl with the pepper (capsicum). Divide the 2 fillings between pastry cases. Return to the oven and cook for a further 15 minutes until just firm.

Makes 12.

POTTED STILTON

225 g (8 oz) Stilton cheese, crumbled
55 g (2 oz/¼ cup) unsalted butter, diced
6 teaspoons brandy
55 g (2 oz/½ cup) chopped walnuts
pinch cayenne pepper
TO FINISH:
25 g (1 oz/6 teaspoons) butter
TO GARNISH:
walnut halves

Put Stilton in a mixing bowl. Add unsalted butter and work into Stilton with a wooden spoon until well blended.

Mix in brandy, chopped nuts and cayenne pepper. Spoon the mixture into 4 small ramekin dishes.

In a small saucepan, melt the remaining butter over a very low heat. Pour the clear liquid over cheese mixture, leaving the milky residue in the pan. Leave to cool. Serve garnished with walnut halves.

Serves 4.

Variation: Instead of Stilton, use finely grated Cheddar cheese. Port may be used instead of brandy, if wished.

CHEESE STRAWS

115 g (4 oz/1 cup) plain flour
pinch salt
½ teaspoon curry powder
55 g (2 oz/¼ cup) butter
55 g (2 oz/½ cup) grated Cheddar cheese
1 egg, beaten
TO FINISH:
poppy and cumin seeds

Sift flour, salt and curry powder into a bowl. Rub in butter until mixture resembles fine breadcrumbs. Add cheese and half the egg and mix to form a dough. Cover and chill for 30 minutes.

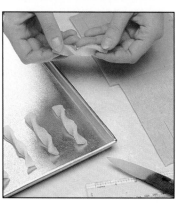

Preheat oven to 200C (400F/Gas 6). Butter several baking sheets. Roll out dough on a floured surface to 0.5cm (¼ in) thickness. Cut into 7.5 x 1 cm (3 x ½ in) strips. Twist and place on baking sheets.

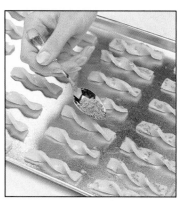

Brush straws with remaining egg. Sprinkle half the straws with poppy seeds and half with cumin seeds. Bake in the oven for 10-15 minutes until golden.

Makes 24-30.

SCOTCH EGGS

225 g (8 oz) pork sausagemeat
1 tablespoon chopped fresh chives
salt and pepper
8 hard-boiled quails' eggs
flour, for coating
1 egg, beaten
85 g (3 oz/1½ cups) fresh white breadcrumbs

Put sausagemeat in a bowl. Mix in chives, and salt and pepper. Divide into 8 equal portions. On a floured surface, flatten each piece into a 5 cm (2 in) circle.

Shell eggs and dust with flour. Put beaten egg in one dish and breadcrumbs in another. Place each egg on a circle of sausagemeat. Mould sausagemeat round egg, sealing the joins well.

Roll each one in beaten egg, then in bread-crumbs. One-third fill a deep fat fryer with vegetable oil and heat to 185C/360F. Carefully put eggs into oil and deep fry for 3-4 minutes until golden brown. Drain on absorbent kitchen paper and leave until cold.

Makes 8.

Variation: Instead of quails' eggs use 4 hens' eggs and cook for 5-6 minutes.

──── SCONES ────

225 g (8 oz/2 cups) self-raising flour, plus extra
   for dusting
1 teaspoon baking powder
55 g (2 oz/¼ cup) butter
25 g (1 oz/5 teaspoons) caster sugar
150 ml (5 fl oz/⅔ cup) milk
TO SERVE:
butter or whipped cream and jam

Preheat the oven to 220C (425F/Gas 7). Dust
a baking sheet with flour. Sift the flour and
baking powder into a bowl and stir to mix.
Rub in butter and stir in sugar.

Make a well in the mixture and pour in milk.
Using a knife, mix together until dough is
soft, but not sticky. Turn onto a floured
surface and knead lightly. Pat dough out to a
thickness of 1 cm (½ in).

Using a 5 cm (2 in) round cutter, cut out 12
scones. Arrange on prepared baking sheet
and dust the tops with flour. Bake in the oven
for 10-12 minutes until well risen and light
brown. Remove to a wire rack and cover with
a cloth while cooling. Serve with butter or
whipped cream and jam.

Makes 12.

Variation: For Cheese Scones, omit caster
sugar and stir in 60 g (2 oz/½ cup) grated
Cheddar cheese instead.

SCOTCH PANCAKES

PANCAKES:
225 g (8 oz/2 cups) self-raising flour
2 teaspoons baking powder
pinch salt
25 g (1 oz/5 teaspoons) caster sugar
1 egg, beaten
225 ml (8 fl oz/1 cup) milk
ORANGE BUTTER:
175 g (6 oz/¾ cup) unsalted butter
25 g (1 oz/2 tablespoons) icing sugar, sifted
6 teaspoons fresh orange juice
grated rind of ½ orange

To make orange butter, in a bowl, beat together all the ingredients until light and fluffy. To make pancakes, sift flour, baking powder and salt into a bowl. Stir in sugar and make a well in the centre. In a bowl, mix together egg and milk and pour into the well. Gradually draw flour into liquid by stirring with a wooden spoon, then beat well to make a smooth batter.

Slowly heat a greased griddle or heavy frying pan. Drop dessertspoonfuls of mixture onto the hot surface and cook for about 3 minutes until bubbles burst on the surface and the underside is golden. Turn pancakes over with a palette knife and cook for a further minute until golden on second side. Wrap in a cloth to keep warm until all pancakes are cooked. Serve with the orange butter.

Makes 20-24 pancakes.

APPLE SCONE ROUND

225 g (8 oz/2 cups) plain flour
2 teaspoons baking powder
115 g (4 oz/½ cup) butter
2 dessert apples
115 g (4 oz/½ cup) caster sugar
55 g (2 oz/⅓ cup) sultanas
1 egg, beaten
TO FINISH:
1 tablespoon demerara sugar
TO SERVE:
butter

Preheat oven to 180C (350F/Gas 4). Grease a 20 cm (8 in) cake tin. Sift flour and baking powder into a bowl.

Rub in butter until mixture resembles breadcrumbs. Peel and core apples, cut into small dice and stir into flour and butter mixture with sugar and sultanas. Mix in beaten egg to form a soft dough. Press mixture into prepared tin. Sprinkle demerara sugar on top.

Bake in the oven for 40-50 minutes until risen and golden brown. Turn out onto a wire rack and leave until just warm. Cut scone in half horizontally. Spread base with butter and replace top. Cut into wedges and serve.

Makes 8 wedges.

BRAMBLE MUFFINS

300 g (10 oz/2½ cups) plain flour
3 teaspoons baking powder
115 g (4 oz/½ cup) caster sugar
1 egg
300 ml (10 fl oz/1⅓ cups) milk
85 ml (3 fl oz/⅓ cup) sunflower oil
few drops vanilla essence
175 g (6 oz) blackberries
TO FINISH:
6 teaspoons demerara sugar

Preheat oven to 200C (400F/Gas 6). Grease a 12-hole muffin or deep bun tin. Sift flour and baking powder into a bowl, then stir in the caster sugar.

In a bowl, beat together egg, milk, sunflower oil and vanilla essence. Add to dry ingredients all at once. Mix until blended. Gently stir in blackberries.

Spoon batter into prepared muffin tin. Sprinkle with demerara sugar. Bake in the oven for 15-20 minutes until well risen and golden brown. Cool in the tin for 5 minutes, then transfer to wire racks to cool completely.

Makes 12.

WELSH CAKES

225 g (8 oz/2 cups) self-raising flour
pinch salt
55 g (2 oz/¼ cup) white cooking fat
55 g (2 oz/¼ cup) margarine
85 g (3 oz/⅓ cup) caster sugar
85 g (3 oz/⅔ cup) currants
1 egg, beaten
3 teaspoons milk (optional)
TO FINISH:
caster sugar, for dusting

Sift flour and salt into a bowl. Rub in white fat and margarine until mixture resembles breadcrumbs. Stir in sugar and currants.

Add egg and a little milk, if necessary, to make a soft, but not sticky dough. On a floured surface, roll out dough to 0.5 cm (¼ in) thickness. Cut into rounds with a 6 cm (2½ in) plain or fluted cutter.

Heat a greased griddle or heavy frying pan. Cook the cakes, over a low heat, for about 3 minutes on each side until golden brown. Dust with caster sugar.

Makes about 16.

— CHOCOLATE NUT MUFFINS —

115 g (4 oz) plain (dark) chocolate
225 g (8 oz/2 cups) plain flour
3 teaspoons baking powder
½ teaspoon ground cinnamon
55 g (2 oz/⅓ cup) soft brown sugar
115 g (4 oz/1 cup) roughly chopped walnuts
225 ml (8 fl oz/1 cup) milk
55 ml (2 fl oz/¼ cup) sunflower oil
few drops vanilla essence
1 egg

Preheat oven to 200C (400F/Gas 6). Grease a
12-hole muffin or deep bun tin.

Break chocolate into pieces and put in a bowl
over a pan of simmering water until melted.
Remove from heat.

Sift flour, baking powder and cinnamon into
bowl of chocolate. Add sugar and nuts. In a
bowl, mix together milk, sunflower oil,
vanilla essence and egg, add to dry
ingredients and stir until blended. Spoon
mixture into prepared tin. Bake in the oven
for 15-20 minutes until well risen and firm.
Cool in the tin for 5 minutes. Remove to a
wire rack to cool completely.

Makes 12.

—DATE & WALNUT LOAF—

225 g (8 oz) stoned dates
grated rind and juice 1 lemon
175 g (6 oz/¾ cup) butter
175 g (6 oz/1 cup) light soft brown sugar
3 eggs, beaten
175 g (6 oz/1½ cups) self-raising flour
55 g (2 oz/½ cup) chopped walnuts
TO FINISH:
8 walnut halves

Preheat oven to 170C (325F/Gas 3). Grease and base line a 1 kg (2.2 lb) loaf tin. Chop dates into small pieces.

Put dates in a saucepan with lemon rind and juice and 70 ml (2½ fl oz/⅓ cup) water and cook for 5 minutes until a soft purée. In a bowl, beat butter and sugar together until light and fluffy. Gradually beat in eggs. Fold in flour and chopped walnuts. Spread one-third of mixture over base of prepared tin. Spread half the date purée over. Repeat layers, ending with cake mixture.

Arrange halved walnuts in a line down centre of loaf. Bake in the oven for 1-1½ hours until well risen and firm to the touch. Leave in tin for 10 minutes, then remove to a wire rack to cool. Serve sliced.

Makes 10-12 slices.

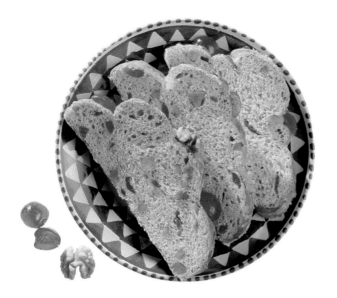

CHERRY NUT BREAD

350 g (12 oz/3 cups) strong plain white flour
½ teaspoon salt
1 teaspoon sugar
2 teaspoons easy blend dried yeast
55 g (2 oz/¼ cup) butter
55 g (2 oz/⅓ cup) glacé cherries, chopped
55 g (2 oz/½ cup) chopped walnuts
150 ml (5 fl oz/⅔ cup) tepid milk
70 ml (2½ fl oz/⅓ cup) tepid water
1 egg, beaten
TOPPING:
85 g (3 oz/½ cup) icing sugar, sifted
25 g (1 oz/2 tablespoons) glacé cherries
25 g (1 oz/⅓ cup) walnut halves

Grease and flour a baking sheet. Sift flour
into a bowl. Stir in salt, sugar and yeast. Rub
in butter and add chopped cherries and
walnuts. Make a well in centre. Pour in milk,
tepid water and egg. Mix to a soft dough.
Turn onto a floured surface and knead for 10
minutes until smooth. Put in an oiled bowl,
cover and leave in a warm place until doubled
in size. Turn dough onto a floured surface,
knead lightly and divide into 5 pieces. Roll
each out to a rope 30 cm (12 in) long.

Plait 3 ropes together and place on prepared
baking sheet. Twist the remaining 2 ropes
together and place on top. Cover with oiled
plastic wrap. Leave in a warm place until
doubled in size. Preheat oven to 220C (425F/
Gas 7). Bake bread in oven for 10 minutes;
reduce heat to 190C (375F/Gas 5); bake for a
further 20 minutes. Cool. Mix icing sugar
with enough water to give a runny icing;
drizzle over loaf. Decorate top with glacé
cherries and walnut halves.

Makes about 12 slices.

CARAWAY KUGELHOPF

225 g (8 oz/2 cups) plain flour
55 g (2 oz/¼ cup) caster sugar
2 teaspoons easy blend yeast
6 teaspoons caraway seeds
55 ml (2 fl oz/¼ cup) tepid water
115 g (4 oz/½ cup) unsalted butter, melted
3 eggs, beaten
TO FINISH:
icing sugar

Grease a 20 cm (8 in) kugelhopf mould. Sift flour into a bowl. Stir in sugar, yeast and caraway seeds.

Make a well in the centre; stir in water, butter and eggs. Beat vigorously until smooth. Cover bowl with plastic wrap and leave in a warm place until doubled in size. Stir mixture and turn into prepared mould. Cover with plastic wrap and leave to rise again until doubled in size.

Preheat oven to 200C (400F/Gas 6). Remove plastic wrap. Bake kugelhopf in the oven for 20 minutes. Lower the temperature to 190C (375F/Gas 5) and bake for a further 10 minutes until well risen and golden brown. Leave in the tin for 10 minutes, then remove to a wire rack. Dust lightly with icing sugar. Serve with butter while still slightly warm.

Makes 8-10 slices.

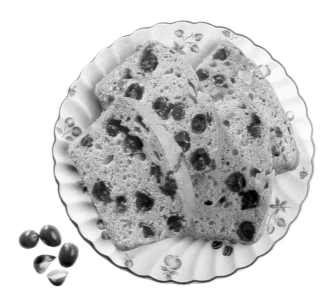

──CRANBERRY BRAZIL LOAF──

225 g (8 oz/2 cups) plain flour
3 teaspoons baking powder
1 teaspoon ground cinnamon
115 g (4 oz/½ cup) caster sugar
2 eggs
grated rind 1 orange
115 ml (4 fl oz/½ cup) orange juice
55 g (2 oz/½ cup) chopped Brazil nuts
175 g (6 oz) cranberries
70 g (2½ oz/¼ cup plus 3 teaspoons) butter, melted
TO SERVE:
butter

Preheat oven to 180C (350F/Gas 4). Grease and line a 1 kg (2.2 lb) loaf tin.

Sift flour, baking powder and cinnamon into a bowl. Stir in sugar and make a well in centre. In a bowl, beat eggs with orange rind and juice. Pour into dry ingredients and mix lightly together.

Stir in Brazil nuts, cranberries and melted butter. Pour into prepared tin. Bake in oven for 50 minutes until well risen and browned. Transfer from tin to a wire rack to cool. When cold, wrap in foil and keep for 24 hours before serving. Serve sliced with butter.

Makes 10-12 slices.

—— LEEK & BACON KNOTS ——

1 leek, finely chopped
55 g (2 oz/¼ cup) butter
175 g (6 oz) streaky bacon, chopped
225 g (8 oz/2 cups) strong plain white flour
225 g (8 oz/2 cups) plain wholemeal flour
1 teaspoon salt
1 teaspoon caster sugar
2 teaspoons easy blend dried yeast
150 ml (5 fl oz/⅔ cup) tepid milk
175 ml (6 fl oz/¾ cup) tepid water
TO FINISH:
beaten egg and sesame seeds

Put leek and half the butter in frying pan. Cook until leek is soft. Remove from pan.

Gently cook bacon in frying pan until fat begins to run. Continue cooking until just beginning to turn crisp. Leave to cool. Sift white flour into a bowl. Stir in wholemeal flour, salt, sugar and yeast. Rub in remaining butter. Stir in leek and bacon and make a well in centre. Pour in milk and tepid water. Stir until a soft dough is formed. Turn out onto a floured surface and knead for about 10 minutes until smooth. Put in an oiled bowl, cover and leave in a warm place until doubled in size.

Grease 2 baking sheets. Turn dough onto a floured surface; knead for 3-4 minutes until smooth. Divide into 12 pieces and roll each into a sausage about 30 cm (12 in) long. Tie each one in a knot and place on baking sheets. Cover with plastic wrap and leave in a warm place until doubled in size. Preheat oven to 220C (425F/Gas 7). Brush rolls with egg and sprinkle with sesame seeds. Bake in the oven for 15 minutes until golden.

Makes 12.

CHEESE & CHIVE PLAIT

450 g (1 lb/4 cups) strong plain white flour
1 teaspoon salt
1 teaspoon caster sugar
1½ teaspoons easy blend dried yeast
25 g (1 oz/6 teaspoons) butter
115 g (4 oz/1 cup) coarsely grated Cheddar cheese
3 tablespoons chopped fresh chives
4 spring onions, chopped
150 ml (5 fl oz/⅔ cup) tepid milk
175 ml (6 fl oz/¾ cup) tepid water
beaten egg, to glaze

Sift flour into a bowl. Stir in salt, sugar and yeast. Rub in butter.

Stir in cheese, chives and spring onions and make a well in the centre. Mix milk with the tepid water and pour into the well. Mix until a soft dough is formed. Turn dough onto a lightly floured surface. Knead for about 10 minutes until smooth and elastic. Place in an oiled bowl, cover and leave in a warm place for about 1 hour, until doubled in size. Preheat oven to 220C (425F/Gas 7). Turn dough out onto a floured surface and knead for about 3 minutes.

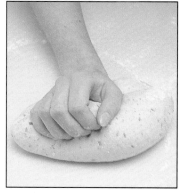

Divide dough into 3 pieces. Roll each one out to a rope shape and plait together, pinching ends to seal. Place on a baking sheet, cover with oiled plastic wrap and leave in a warm place for about 45 minutes until doubled in size. Brush with beaten egg and bake in the oven for 20 minutes. Reduce temperature to 180C (350F/Gas 4) and bake for a further 15 minutes until golden brown and the base sounds hollow when tapped. Serve loaf warm or cold.

Makes about 10 slices.

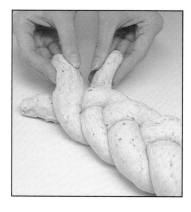

CHELSEA BUNS

225 g (8 oz/2 cups) strong plain white flour
2 teaspoons easy blend dried yeast
1 teaspoon caster sugar
½ teaspoon salt
6 teaspoons unsalted butter
115 ml (4 fl oz/½ cup) tepid milk
1 egg, beaten
FILLING:
55 g (2 oz/¼ cup) unsalted butter, softened
55 g (2 oz/⅓ cup) soft light brown sugar
115 g (4 oz/¾ cup) mixed dried fruit
1 teaspoon mixed spice
TO FINISH:
85 g (3 oz/½ cup) icing sugar

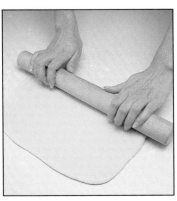

Butter a 17.5 cm (7 in) square cake tin. Sift flour into a bowl. Stir in yeast, caster sugar and salt. Rub in butter. Make a well in the centre. Pour in the tepid milk and egg. Beat vigorously to make a soft dough. On a floured surface, knead dough for 5-10 minutes until smooth. Put dough in an oiled bowl, cover and leave in a warm place for about 1 hour until doubled in size. Turn dough out onto a floured surface. Knead lightly; roll out to a rectangle 30 x 22.5 cm (12 x 9 in).

Spread with softened butter and sprinkle with brown sugar, fruit and spice. Roll up from a long side and cut into 9 pieces. Place in tin, cut sides up. Cover with oiled plastic wrap. Leave in a warm place for 45 minutes until well risen. Preheat oven to 190C (375F/Gas 5). Bake in oven for 30 minutes until golden. Leave to cool in tin for 10 minutes, then transfer, in one piece, to a wire rack to cool. Mix icing sugar with enough water to make a thin glaze. Brush over buns.

Makes 9.

LEMON & CURRANT BRIOCHES

225 g (8 oz/2 cups) strong plain white flour
2 teaspoons easy blend dried yeast
½ teaspoon salt
3 teaspoons caster sugar
55 g (2 oz/⅓ cup) currants
grated rind 1 lemon
6 teaspoons tepid water
2 eggs, beaten
55 g (2 oz/¼ cup) unsalted butter, melted
TO GLAZE:
beaten egg

Butter 12 individual brioche tins. Sift flour into a bowl; stir in yeast, salt, sugar, currants and lemon rind.

Make a well in the centre. Pour in water, eggs and melted butter and beat vigorously to make a soft dough. Turn onto a lightly floured surface and knead for 5 minutes until smooth and elastic. Put dough in an oiled bowl; cover and leave in a warm place for 1 hour until doubled in size. Turn out onto a lightly floured surface, re-knead and roll into a rope shape. Cut into 12 equal pieces. Shape three-quarters of each piece into a ball and place in prepared tins.

With a floured finger, press a hole in centre of each. Shape remaining pieces of dough into a little plug and press into holes, flattening the top slightly. Place tins on a baking sheet. Cover with oiled plastic wrap and leave in a warm place until dough comes almost to top of tins. Preheat oven to 220C (425F/Gas 7). Brush brioches with beaten egg. Bake in the oven for 15 minutes until golden brown. Serve warm with butter and jam.

Makes 12.

CRUMPETS

450 g (1 lb/4 cups) strong plain white flour
1 teaspoon salt
1 teaspoon caster sugar
2 teaspoons easy blend dried yeast
550 ml (20 fl oz/2½ cups) tepid milk
150 ml (5 fl oz/⅔ cup) tepid water
oil, for cooking
TO SERVE:
butter

Sift flour into a bowl. Stir in salt, sugar and yeast.

Make a well in the centre of flour and pour in the tepid milk and water. With a wooden spoon, gradually work flour into liquid, then beat vigorously to make a smooth batter. Cover bowl with a cloth and leave in a warm place for about 1 hour or until mixture has doubled in size.

Thoroughly grease a heavy frying pan or griddle and several crumpet rings. Arrange as many rings as possible in the pan. Heat the pan and pour in enough of the mixture to half fill each ring. Cook crumpets for 5-6 minutes until bubbles appear and burst on the surface. Remove rings and turn crumpets over. Cook on other side for a further 2-3 minutes. Serve crumpets hot, generously buttered.

Makes about 16.

DEVONSHIRE SPLITS

55 g (2 oz/¼ cup) unsalted butter
6 teaspoons caster sugar
150 ml (5 fl oz/⅔ cup) milk
450 g (1 lb/4 cups) strong plain white flour
2 teaspoons easy blend dried yeast
½ teaspoon salt
FILLING:
115 g (4 oz/⅓ cup) strawberry jam
300 ml (10 fl oz/1¼ cups) double (thick) cream,
   whipped
TO FINISH:
icing sugar, for dusting

In a saucepan, heat butter, sugar, milk and 150 ml (5 fl oz/⅔ cup) water until butter has melted and sugar dissolved. Leave liquid until tepid. Sift flour into a bowl. Stir in yeast and salt. Make a well in the centre, pour in liquid and mix vigorously to a soft dough. Turn onto a floured surface and knead until smooth. Place in an oiled bowl, cover and leave in a warm place until the mixture has doubled in size. Preheat oven to 220C (425F/Gas 7). Grease 2 baking sheets.

Turn dough out onto a floured surface. Divide into 16 pieces. Knead each piece lightly and shape into a ball. Place on baking sheets, flattening each ball slightly. Cover with oiled plastic wrap and leave in a warm place for about 40 minutes until well risen. Bake in the oven for about 15 minutes until bases sound hollow when tapped. Cool on a wire rack. Split and fill with jam and cream. Dust lightly with icing sugar.

Makes 16.

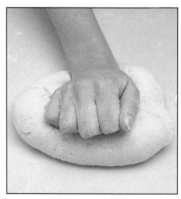

LEMON CRUNCH CAKE

115 g (4 oz/½ cup) butter or margarine, softened
175 g (6 oz/¾ cup) caster sugar
2 eggs, beaten
finely grated rind 1 lemon
175 g (6 oz/1½ cups) self-raising flour
55 ml (2 fl oz/¼ cup) milk
TOPPING:
juice 1 lemon
115 g (4 oz/½ cup) granulated sugar

Preheat oven to 180C (350F/Gas 4). Grease and line a shallow oblong tin measuring 17.5 x 22.5 x 2.5 cm (7 x 9 x 1 in) and line with non-stick paper. In a bowl, beat together butter or margarine and sugar until light and fluffy.

Gradually beat in eggs. Stir in lemon rind. Fold in sifted flour, alternately with milk. Turn mixture into prepared tin and level surface. Bake in the oven for about 50 minutes until well risen and pale golden.

While cake is baking, make topping. In a bowl, mix together lemon juice and sugar. Spoon topping over hot cake. Leave in tin until completely cold, then turn out and cut into squares or diamonds.

Makes 12 squares or diamonds.

GINGER CAKE

225 g (8 oz/2 cups) self-raising flour
3 teaspoons ground ginger
1 teaspoon ground cinnamon
½ teaspoon bicarbonate of soda
115 g (4 oz/½ cup) butter or margarine
115 g (4 oz/¾ cup) light soft brown sugar
2 eggs
5 teaspoons golden syrup
5 teaspoons milk
TOPPING:
3 pieces stem ginger
115 g (4 oz/¾ cup) icing sugar
4 teaspoons stem ginger syrup

Preheat oven to 160C (325F/Gas 3). Grease a shallow oblong tin measuring 27.5 x 17.5 cm (11 x 7 in) and line with non-stick paper. Sift flour, ginger, cinnamon and bicarbonate of soda into a bowl. Rub in butter, then stir in sugar. In a bowl, whisk together eggs, syrup and milk. Pour into dry ingredients and beat until smooth and glossy. Pour into prepared tin. Bake in the oven for 45-50 minutes until well risen and firm to the touch. Leave in tin for 30 minutes, then remove to a wire rack to cool completely.

Cut each piece of stem ginger into quarters and arrange on top of cake. In a bowl, mix together sifted icing sugar, ginger syrup and sufficient water to make a smooth icing. Put icing into a greaseproof paper icing bag and drizzle over top of cake. Leave to set. Cut cake into squares.

Makes 12 squares.

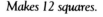

JEWEL-TOPPED MADEIRA CAKE

225 g (8 oz/1 cup) butter, softened
225 g (8 oz/1 ¼ cups) caster sugar
grated rind 1 lemon
4 eggs, beaten
300 g (10 oz/2 ½ cups) self-raising flour
2-3 tablespoons milk
TOPPING:
8 teaspoons clear honey
225 g (8 oz) crystallised fruits and angelica

Preheat oven to 160C (325F/Gas 3). Grease and line a 20 cm (8 in) deep, round cake tin. In a bowl, beat together butter, sugar and lemon rind until light and fluffy.

Gradually beat in eggs. Fold in sifted flour, alternating with sufficient milk to give a soft dropping consistency. Spoon mixture into prepared tin. Bake in the oven for 1½-1¾ hours, until a skewer inserted into the centre of cake comes out clean.

Leave to cool in tin for 5 minutes, then transfer to a wire rack to cool. Gently heat honey. Brush over cake and arrange fruits and angelica on top.

Makes 8-10 slices.

Variation: A traditional Madeira cake has a thin slice of candied peel on top. This should be placed on cake after it has been cooking for about 1 hour.

—COCONUT & CHERRY CAKE—

225 g (8 oz/1 cup) butter, softened
225 g (8 oz/1¼ cups) caster sugar
4 eggs and 1 egg yolk
225 g (8 oz/2 cups) self-raising flour, sifted
55 g (2 oz/⅔ cup) desiccated coconut
175 g (6 oz/1 cup) glacé cherries, rinsed and quartered
TOPPING:
1 egg white
85 g (3 oz/½ cup) icing sugar, sifted
55 g (2 oz/1¼ cups) shredded coconut

Preheat oven to 180C (350F/Gas 4). Grease a
20 cm (8 in) loose-bottomed cake tin and line
with non-stick paper.

In a bowl, beat butter and sugar until light
and fluffy. In a bowl, whisk together eggs and
egg yolk. Gradually beat into creamed
mixture. Fold in flour, desiccated coconut
and cherries. Spoon mixture into prepared
tin and bake in the oven for 45-50 minutes
until just firm.

To make the topping, whisk egg white in a
bowl until stiff; gradually whisk in icing sugar.
Spread over top of cake. Scatter over
shredded coconut. Return to the oven and
cook for a further 20 minutes until golden
brown and a skewer inserted into the centre
of cake comes out clean. Cover lightly with
foil if topping is browning too quickly. Leave
to cool in tin for 10 minutes; transfer to a wire
rack to cool completely.

Makes 8-10 slices.

DUNDEE CAKE

225 g (8 oz/1 cup) butter
225 g (8 oz/1½ cups) soft brown sugar
4 eggs, beaten
300 g (10 oz/2½ cups) plain flour, sifted
a little milk
55 g (2 oz/½ cup) ground almonds
115 g (4 oz/¾ cup) currants
115 g (4 oz/¾ cup) sultanas
115 g (4 oz/¾ cup) raisins
55 g (2 oz/⅓ cup) chopped mixed citrus peel
55 g (2 oz/⅓ cup) glacé cherries
grated rind 1 small orange and 1 small lemon
½ teaspoon bicarbonate of soda, dissolved in
    1 teaspoon milk
55 g (2 oz/⅓ cup) blanched almonds

Preheat oven to 170C (325F/Gas 3). Grease and line a 20 cm (8 in) round cake tin. In a bowl, beat butter and sugar until light and fluffy. Gradually beat in eggs. Fold in flour to give a soft dropping consistency. If necessary, add a little milk. Carefully fold in ground almonds, currants, sultanas, raisins, peel, rinsed, dried and halved cherries and orange and lemon rind. Add bicarbonate of soda dissolved in milk. Stir to mix.

Turn mixture into prepared tin. Smooth the top. Arrange blanched almonds in circles over top of cake. Bake in the oven for 2½-3 hours until a skewer inserted into the centre of the cake comes out clean. Leave to cool in the tin for 30 minutes, then transfer to a wire rack to cool completely.

Makes about 12 slices.

——— APPLE STREUSEL CAKE ———

450 g (1 lb) cooking apples
a little lemon juice
175 g (6 oz/1½ cups) self-raising flour
1 teaspoon baking powder
115 g (4 oz/½ cup) soft margarine
115 g (4 oz/½ cup) caster sugar
2 eggs, beaten
1-2 tablespoons milk
STREUSEL TOPPING:
115 g (4 oz/1 cup) self-raising flour
1 teaspoon ground cinnamon
85 g (3 oz/⅓ cup) butter
85 g (3 oz/⅓ cup) caster sugar
icing sugar, to finish

Preheat oven to 180C (350F/Gas 4). Grease a 22.5 cm (9 in) spring-release tin. To make streusel topping, sift flour and cinnamon into a bowl. Rub in butter until mixture resembles coarse crumbs. Stir in caster sugar; set aside. Peel, core and thinly slice apples. Toss in a little lemon juice.

Sift flour and baking powder into a bowl. Add margarine, sugar and eggs. Beat well until mixture is smooth, adding just enough milk to give a soft dropping consistency. Spoon into prepared tin. Cover with apple slices and sprinkle with streusel topping. Bake in the oven for 1 hour until firm and golden brown. Cool in tin before opening sides. Dust with icing sugar.

Makes 8-10 slices.

Note: Keep cake for 24 hours before serving.

HONEY SPICE CAKE

150 g (5 oz/⅔ cup) **butter or margarine**
115 g (4 oz/¾ cup) **soft light brown sugar**
175 g (6 oz/½ cup) **clear honey**
200 g (7 oz/1¾ cups) **self-raising flour**
1½ teaspoons **ground mixed spice**
2 **eggs, beaten**
ICING:
350 g (12 oz/2¼ cups) **icing sugar**

Preheat oven to 180C (350F/Gas 4). Grease an 850 ml (30 fl oz/3¾ cup) fluted ring mould. Put butter or margarine, sugar, honey and 3 teaspoons water into a saucepan.

Heat gently until butter has melted and sugar has dissolved. Remove from heat and cool for 10 minutes. Sift flour and mixed spice into a bowl. Pour in melted mixture and eggs; beat well until smooth. Pour batter into prepared tin. Bake in the oven for 40-50 minutes until well risen and a skewer inserted into the centre, comes out clean. Leave to cool in the tin for 2-3 minutes, then remove to a wire rack to cool completely.

To make icing, sift icing sugar into a bowl. Stir in about 9 teaspoons water to make a smooth, flowing icing. Spoon carefully over cake so that it is evenly covered in icing.

Makes 8-10 slices.

—CHOCOLATE MARBLE CAKE—

55 g (2 oz) plain (dark) chocolate
3 teaspoons strong coffee
225 g (8 oz/2 cups) self-raising flour
1 teaspoon baking powder
225 g (8 oz/1 cup) soft margarine
225 g (8 oz/1¼ cups) caster sugar
4 eggs, beaten
55 g (2 oz/½ cup) ground almonds
6 teaspoons milk
FROSTING:
130 g (4½ oz) plain (dark) chocolate
25 g (1 oz/6 teaspoons) butter

Preheat oven to 180C (350F/Gas 4). Grease a 1.7 litre (60 fl oz/7½ cup) ring mould. Put chocolate and coffee in a basin. Set over a pan of simmering water; heat until melted. Leave to cool. Sift flour and baking powder into a bowl. Add margarine, sugar, eggs, ground almonds and milk. Beat well until smooth. Spoon half the mixture evenly into prepared tin. Stir cooled, soft chocolate into the remaining mixture, and spoon into tin. Draw a knife through mixture in a spiral. Smooth the surface.

Bake in the oven for 50-60 minutes until well risen and a skewer inserted into the centre, comes out clean. Leave in tin for 5 minutes, then turn out onto a wire rack to cool, completely. To make frosting, put chocolate, butter and 6 teaspoons water in a bowl, then set over a pan of simmering water until melted. Stir and pour over cake, working quickly to coat top and sides. Leave to set before serving.

Makes 10-12 slices.

TOFFEE DATE CAKE

225 g (8 oz/1²⁄₃ cups) chopped dates
300 ml (10 fl oz/1¼ cups) boiling water
115 g (4 oz/½ cup) soft butter
175 g (6 oz/¾ cup) caster sugar
3 eggs, beaten
225 g (8 oz/2 cups) self-raising flour, sifted
½ teaspoon ground cinnamon
1 teaspoon bicarbonate of soda
few drops vanilla essence
TOPPING:
85 g (3 oz/½ cup) soft brown sugar
55 g (2 oz/¼ cup) butter
9 teaspoons double (thick) cream

Cover dates with the boiling water.

Preheat oven to 180C (350F/Gas 4). Grease a 22.5 cm (9 in) spring-release tin. In a bowl, beat butter and sugar until light and fluffy. Gradually beat in eggs. Fold in flour and cinnamon. Add bicarbonate of soda and vanilla essence to dates and water. Pour onto creamed mixture; stir until thoroughly mixed. Pour into prepared tin. Bake in oven for 1-1¼ hours until well risen and firm.

To make topping, put soft brown sugar, butter and cream in a saucepan. Heat gently until sugar is melted. Bring to the boil and simmer for 3 minutes. Pour over cake and put under the grill until topping is bubbling. Leave to cool in tin until toffee is set. Remove to a wire rack to cool completely.

Makes 8-10 slices.

——— PEACH & ORANGE CAKE ———

130 g (4½ oz) can peach slices or halves
175 g (6 oz/¾ cup) butter
225 g (8 oz/1¼ cups) caster sugar
grated rind 1 orange
4 eggs, beaten
150 ml (5 fl oz/⅔ cup) thick sour cream
225 g (8 oz/2 cups) plain flour
½ teaspoon bicarbonate of soda
TO FINISH:
icing sugar and zest of 1 orange

Preheat oven to 180C (350F/Gas 4). Grease a kugelhof mould and dust with flour. Drain peach slices and roughly chop.

In a bowl, beat butter and sugar until light and fluffy. Add orange rind and gradually beat in eggs. Fold in peaches and thick sour cream. Sift flour and bicarbonate of soda onto mixture. Fold in gently and spread into prepared tin. Bake in the oven for 45-50 minutes until well risen and golden brown.

Leave in the tin for 10 minutes, then turn out onto a wire rack to cool completely. Sift icing sugar over cake. Decorate with orange zest.

Makes 8-10 slices.

— BLACKCURRANT WHIRLS —

225 g (8 oz/1 cup) butter
55 g (2 oz/⅓ cup) icing sugar, sifted
few drops almond essence
225 g (8 oz/2 cups) plain flour
55 g (2 oz/2 tablespoons) blackcurrant jam
TO FINISH:
icing sugar, for dusting

Preheat oven to 180C (350F/Gas 4). Arrange 12 paper cases in bun tins. In a bowl, beat butter with icing sugar and almond essence until creamy. Sift flour onto mixture and beat until smooth.

Spoon mixture into a piping bag fitted with a large star nozzle. Pipe whirls into paper cases, to cover the bases. Pipe a ring round the edge to leave a slight hollow in the centre.

Bake in the oven for 20 minutes until set and very lightly browned. Transfer from tins to a wire rack to cool. Put a little jam in the centre of each whirl. Dust lightly with icing sugar.

Makes 12.

– STRAWBERRY-ROSE MERINGUES –

MERINGUES:
2 egg whites
115 g (4 oz/½ cup) caster sugar
FILLING:
150 ml (5 fl oz/⅔ cup) double (thick) cream
55 g (2 oz) strawberries
2 teaspoons icing sugar
12 teaspoons rosewater
TO DECORATE:
12 strawberries

Preheat oven to 120C (250F/Gas ½). Line 2 baking sheets with non-stick paper.

To make meringues, whisk egg whites in a bowl until very stiff; whisk in half sugar. Carefully fold in remaining sugar. Spoon meringue into a piping bag fitted with a large star nozzle. Pipe twenty four 7.5 cm (3 in) lengths onto prepared baking sheets. Bake in the oven for 1 hour until meringues are dry. Cool on wire racks.

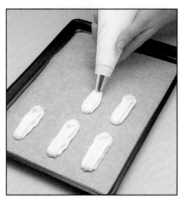

To make filling, whip cream in a bowl, until thick. In a blender or food processor, purée strawberries. Sieve purée into a bowl; stir in icing sugar and rosewater. Add cream and mix well together. Sandwich meringues together with strawberry cream. Decorate with strawberries and serve at once.

Makes 12.

HONEY MADELEINES

55 g (2 oz/¼ cup) butter
2 eggs
55 g (2 oz/¼ cup) caster sugar
3 teaspoons clear honey
55 g (2 oz/½ cup) plain flour
½ teaspoon baking powder
TO FINISH:
icing sugar, for sifting

Preheat oven to 190C (375F/Gas 5). Lightly butter 12 madeleine tins. In a small saucepan, gently heat butter until melted. Leave to cool.

In a bowl, whisk eggs and caster sugar until thick and pale. Stir in melted butter and honey. Sift flour and baking powder onto egg mixture and fold in gently.

Spoon mixture into prepared tins. Bake in the oven for 10 minutes until light golden brown. Leave in tins for 2 minutes, then transfer to a wire rack to cool. Dust lightly with icing sugar.

Makes 12.

Note: If you do not have madeleine tins, these cakes can be made in tartlet tins.

CHOCOLATE BROWNIES

55 g (2 oz/½ cup) plain flour
25 g (1 oz/¼ cup) cocoa
115 g (4 oz/½ cup) butter
225 g (8 oz/1¼ cups) caster sugar
few drops vanilla essence
2 eggs, beaten
55 g (2 oz/½ cup) chopped walnuts
FROSTING:
115 g (4 oz) plain (dark) chocolate
150 ml (5 fl oz/⅔ cup) thick sour cream

Preheat oven to 160C (325F/Gas 3). Butter a
20 cm (8 in) square cake tin. Sift flour and
cocoa onto a plate.

Put butter, sugar and 3 teaspoons cold water
into a saucepan. Stir over a low heat to melt
butter. Remove from heat; stir in vanilla
essence, then beat in eggs, one at a time. Add
flour and cocoa; beat to a smooth shiny
mixture. Stir in walnuts. Pour mixture into
prepared tin. Bake in the oven for 20 minutes
until set. Leave in tin to cool.

To make frosting, break chocolate into a
heatproof bowl. Set bowl over a pan of hot
water until chocolate is melted. Stir until
smooth; remove from the heat. Stir in thick
sour cream; beat until evenly blended. Spoon
topping over brownies and make a swirling
pattern with a palette knife. Leave in a cool
place to set. Cut into squares and remove
from the tin.

Makes 9 large or 16 small brownies.

— STRAWBERRY SHORTCAKE —

SHORTCAKE:
225 g (8 oz/2 cups) plain flour
3 teaspoons baking powder
25 g (1 oz/5 teaspoons) caster sugar
85 g (3 oz/⅓ cup) butter
85 ml (3 fl oz/⅓ cup) milk
FILLING:
700 g (1½ lb) strawberries
55 g (2 oz/¼ cup) caster sugar
300 ml (10 fl oz/1¼ cups) double (thick) cream

Preheat oven to 220C (425F/Gas 7). Grease a baking sheet. Sift flour and baking powder into a bowl.

Stir in sugar; rub in butter until mixture resembles breadcrumbs. Pour in milk and mix to form a soft dough. On a floured surface, roll out dough to 0.5 cm (¼ in) thickness. Cut into eight 7.5 cm (3 in) rounds. Place on prepared baking sheet. Bake in the oven for 10-12 minutes until golden brown. Slice most of strawberries, reserving a few for decoration. In a bowl, mix together sliced strawberries and sugar. In a bowl, whip cream until thick.

Split shortcakes in half while still warm; spread bottom halves with two-thirds of cream. Cover cream with sliced strawberries and top with other halves of shortcake. Add a swirl of cream to each one and decorate with reserved strawberries.

Makes 8.

CHERRY NUT ROCKIES

115 g (4 oz/²⁄₃ cup) glacé cherries
55 g (2 oz/½ cup) walnuts
225 g (8 oz/2 cups) plain flour
2 teaspoons baking powder
½ teaspoon mixed spice
175 g (6 oz/1 cup) soft brown sugar
175 g (6 oz/¾ cup) butter
1 egg, beaten
3-6 teaspoons milk (optional)

Preheat oven to 190C (375F/Gas 5). Grease a baking sheet. Cut cherries into quarters; coarsely chop walnuts.

Sift flour, baking powder and mixed spice into a bowl. Stir in sugar. Rub in butter until mixture resembles breadcrumbs. Stir in cherries and nuts. In a bowl, whisk egg lightly and stir into flour mixture to form a stiff dough. Add a little milk if necessary.

Using 2 forks, pile the mixture in rocky heaps on prepared baking sheet. Bake in the oven for 15-20 minutes until golden brown and firm. Leave to cool on baking sheet for 2 minutes, then transfer to a wire rack to cool completely.

Makes 10-12.

SPONGE DROPS

SPONGE:
55 g (2 oz/½ cup) plain flour
2 large eggs
55 g (2 oz/¼ cup) caster sugar
caster sugar, for sprinkling
FILLING:
150 ml (5 fl oz/⅔ cup) double (thick) cream
4 teaspoons red jam

Preheat oven to 190C (375F/Gas 5). Grease several baking sheets and line with grease-proof paper. Sift flour into a bowl. In a bowl, whisk together the eggs and sugar until pale and thick.

Sift flour again, into mixture and fold in very gently. Put mixture in a piping bag fitted with a 1 cm (½ in) plain nozzle. Pipe mixture onto prepared baking sheets in rounds of 4 cm (1½ in). Sprinkle drops with caster sugar. Bake in the oven for 10 minutes until light golden. Slide the paper with sponge drops still attached, off the baking sheet onto a damp tea towel. Leave until cold.

In a bowl, whisk cream until thick. Remove sponge drops from the paper. Sandwich together in pairs with a little jam and whipped cream.

Makes 18.

——— GINGER BRANDY SNAPS ———

BRANDY SNAPS:
55 g (2 oz/¼ cup) unsalted butter
55 g (2 oz/¼ cup) demerara sugar
55 g (2 oz/2 tablespoons) golden syrup
55 g (2 oz/½ cup) plain flour
½ teaspoon ground ginger
1 teaspoon brandy
FILLING:
300 ml (10 fl oz/1¼ cups) double (thick) cream
3 teaspoons stem ginger syrup
6 pieces stem ginger

Preheat oven to 180C (350F/Gas 4).

Grease several baking sheets. Butter the handles of 3 or 4 wooden spoons. Put butter, demerara sugar and syrup in a saucepan and heat gently until butter has melted and sugar dissolved. Cool slightly. Sift flour and ginger into melted ingredients and stir in with the brandy. Drop teaspoonfuls of mixture, well spaced out, onto prepared baking sheets. Bake in the oven for 7-10 minutes until brandy snaps are golden.

Quickly remove brandy snaps from baking sheets and roll round spoon handles, leaving them in place until set. Slide off spoons; leave on wire racks until completely cold. In a bowl, whisk cream with ginger syrup until thick. Put cream into a piping bag fitted with a small star nozzle. Pipe into each end of brandy snaps. Slice pieces of stem ginger and use to decorate brandy snaps.

Makes about 18.

QUEEN CAKES

55 g (2 oz/⅓ cup) currants
115 g (4 oz/1 cup) self-raising flour
55 g (2 oz/¼ cup) butter
55 g (2 oz/¼ cup) caster sugar
1 egg
finely grated rind 1 lemon
3 teaspoons double (thick) cream

Preheat the oven to 180C (350F/Gas 4). Thoroughly butter 9 individual brioche tins. Put currants into bases of tins. Stand tins on a baking sheet.

Sift flour into a bowl and set aside. In a bowl, beat together the butter and sugar until creamy. Mix together egg and lemon rind and gradually beat into creamed mixture. Add half the flour and fold in lightly. Add the remaining flour and cream and mix to a smooth consistency.

Spoon mixture into tins on top of currants. Bake in the oven for 15-20 minutes until golden. Turn out of tins while still hot. Leave on a wire rack to cool completely. Serve currant sides up.

Makes 9.

Note: If you do not have brioche tins, use paper cases placed in bun tins.

──LEMON BUTTERFLY CAKES──

85 g (3 oz/⅓ cup) butter
85 g (3 oz/⅓ cup) caster sugar
1 egg, beaten
115 g (4 oz/1 cup) self-raising flour
grated rind ½ lemon
3-6 tablespoons milk
ICING:
55 g (2 oz/¼ cup) butter, softened
115 g (4 oz/¾ cup) icing sugar, sifted
3 teaspoons lemon juice
TO DECORATE:
a few black and green grapes

Preheat oven to 190C (375F/Gas 5). Put 12 paper cases into bun tins.

In a bowl, beat together butter and sugar until creamy. Gradually add egg to creamed mixture, beating well after each addition. Add half the flour and all the lemon rind and fold in lightly. Add remaining flour and sufficient milk to give a medium soft consistency. Spoon mixture into paper cases. Bake in the oven for 15-20 minutes until well risen and brown. Allow to cool.

When cakes are cool, cut a shallow cone from the centre of each one; reserve. To make filling, in a bowl, beat together the butter and icing sugar until creamy. Add lemon juice and beat until smooth and well blended. Fill the hollow in top of cakes with lemon buttercream. Cut the reserved cones in half and arrange in buttercream to resemble wings. Cut the grapes into quarters and use them to decorate cakes.

Makes 12.

──── SUMMER SPONGE CAKE ────

175 g (6 oz/¾ cup) soft butter
175 g (6 oz/¾ cup) caster sugar
3 eggs, beaten
175 g (6 oz/1½ cups) self-raising flour
4 teaspoons boiling water
FILLING:
85 g (3 oz/⅓ cup) soft unsalted butter
115 g (4 oz/¾ cup) icing sugar, sifted
few drops vanilla essence
ICING:
175 g (6 oz/1 cup) icing sugar, sifted
2 teaspoons lemon juice
TO DECORATE:
crystallised flowers

Preheat oven to 180C (350F/Gas 4). Grease two 20 cm (8 in) sandwich tins and line bases with non-stick paper. In a bowl, beat together butter and sugar until light and fluffy. Gradually beat in eggs, then fold in flour. Stir in the boiling water to make a soft dropping consistency. Divide mixture between prepared tins. Bake in the oven for 25-30 minutes until cakes are lightly browned and spring back when pressed. Leave in tins for 5 minutes, then transfer to wire racks to cool.

To make filling, in a bowl, beat together the unsalted butter and icing sugar. Stir in vanilla essence. Sandwich cakes together with filling. To make icing, in a bowl, mix together icing sugar, lemon juice and sufficient water to make a spreading consistency. Spread icing over cake and decorate with crystallised flowers.

Makes 8 slices.

——— STRAWBERRY ROULADE ———

6 eggs
200 g (7 oz/1 cup) caster sugar
2 teaspoons baking powder
175 g (6 oz/1⅔ cups) ground almonds
FILLING:
150 g (5 oz/⅔ cup) cream cheese
150 ml (5 fl oz/⅔ cup) double (thick) cream
225 g (8 oz) strawberries
2 passion fruit
TO DECORATE:
icing sugar
a few whole strawberries

Preheat oven to 180C (350F/Gas 4). Grease a
37.5 x 25 cm (15 x 10 in) Swiss roll tin and
line base and sides with non-stick paper.

Separate eggs. In a bowl, whisk whites until
stiff but not dry. In another bowl, beat
together egg yolks and sugar until pale and
thick. Mix baking powder thoroughly into
ground almonds. Stir gently into yolk
mixture, without overmixing. Carefully fold
in egg whites. Spread in tin. Bake in oven for
15 minutes until firm. Cover with a tea towel
and leave to cool in tin.

In a bowl, beat cream cheese and cream.
Reserve one-third. Mash half the strawberries; chop remainder. Scoop out passion
fruit flesh and stir into cream with mashed
strawberries. Place a sheet of greaseproof
paper on a work surface; dust thickly with
icing sugar. Turn roulade out onto paper. Peel
off lining paper. Spread cream over roulade;
scatter over chopped strawberries. Roll up
and pipe reserved cream on top. Decorate
with the whole strawberries.

Serves 6-8.

– DOUBLE CHOCOLATE GÂTEAU –

225 g (8 oz/1 cup) soft butter
225 g (8 oz/1¼ cups) caster sugar
4 eggs, beaten
175 g (6 oz/1½ cups) self-raising flour
55 g (2 oz/½ cup) cocoa
FILLING:
250 ml (9 fl oz/1 cup) whipping cream
150 g (5 oz) white chocolate
FROSTING:
350 g (12 oz) plain (dark) chocolate
115 g (4 oz/½ cup) butter
85 ml (3 fl oz/⅓ cup) double (thick) cream
TO DECORATE:
115 g (4 oz) plain (dark) chocolate
2 teaspoons icing sugar and cocoa mixed

To make the filling, heat the cream in a saucepan to just below boiling point. In a food processor, chop white chocolate. With motor running, pour hot cream through feed tube and process for 10-15 seconds until smooth. Transfer to a bowl, cover with plastic wrap and chill overnight. The next day whisk the filling until just beginning to hold soft peaks.

To make chocolate curls for decoration, melt chocolate in a bowl over a pan of hot water. Spread one-quarter of the chocolate over a baking sheet. Chill sheet for a few minutes until chocolate loses its gloss and is just set, but not hard. Using a palette knife, scrape off large shavings of chocolate, transferring them to a baking sheet lined with non-stick paper. Chill until set. Make 3 more batches of shavings in the same way.

Preheat oven to 180C (350F/Gas 4). Grease a 20 cm (8 in) deep round tin and line the base with non-stick paper. In bowl, beat together butter and sugar until light and fluffy. Gradually beat in eggs. Sift together flour and cocoa. Fold into mixture, then spoon into tin. Bake in the oven for 45-50 minutes until springy to the touch and a skewer inserted into the centre comes out clean. Leave in tin for 5 minutes, then remove to a wire rack to cool completely.

To make the frosting, melt chocolate in a bowl over pan of hot water. Stir in butter and cream. Leave to cool, stirring occasionally until mixture is a thick spreading consistency.

Slice the cake horizontally into 3 layers. Sandwich layers together with white chocolate filling. Cover top and sides of cake with chocolate frosting. Arrange chocolate shavings over top of cake. Sift mixed icing sugar and cocoa over cake.

Makes 10 slices.

—CHOC ALMOND MERINGUE—

MERINGUE:
4 egg whites
225 g (8 oz/1¼ cups) caster sugar
115 g (4 oz/1¼ cups) ground almonds
FILLING:
175 g (6 oz) plain (dark) chocolate
45 g (1½ oz/9 teaspoons) unsalted butter
9 teaspoons black coffee
9 teaspoons brandy
175 ml (6 fl oz/¾ cup) whipping cream
TO DECORATE:
chopped, toasted almonds

Preheat oven to 140C (275F/Gas 1). Line 2 baking sheets with non-stick paper.

To make meringue, whisk egg whites in a bowl until stiff; whisk in half the sugar. In another bowl, mix together remaining sugar and ground almonds. Carefully fold into meringue mixture. Pipe or spread meringue in two 20 cm (8 in) rounds on the prepared baking sheets. Bake in the oven for about 1½ hours until completely dry. Transfer to wire racks to cool.

To make filling, break chocolate into pieces and put into a bowl with butter, coffee and brandy. Set over a pan of simmering water. When melted, stir and set aside to cool. Whip cream lightly; stir in chocolate mixture. Sandwich meringue rounds together with most of the chocolate cream. Put remaining cream into a piping bag and pipe rosettes on top of cake. Decorate with toasted almonds.

Serves 8.

——FROSTED WALNUT CAKE——

175 g (6 oz/¾ cup) soft butter
175 g (6 oz/¾ cup) caster sugar
3 eggs, beaten
55 g (2 oz/½ cup) chopped walnuts
175 g (6 oz/1½ cups) self-raising flour
FROSTING:
225 g (8 oz/1¼ cups) caster sugar
2 egg whites
6 walnut halves

Preheat oven to 180C (350F/Gas 4). Grease two 20 cm (8 in) deep round cake tins and line bases with non-stick paper. In a bowl, beat together butter and sugar until light and fluffy.

Gradually beat in eggs. Fold in walnuts and sifted flour. Divide mixture between prepared tins. Bake in the oven for 25-35 minutes until risen and golden brown. Leave in the tins for 5 minutes, then transfer to wire racks to cool. To make frosting, put sugar in a saucepan with 70 ml (2½ fl oz/⅓ cup) water. Stir over low heat until sugar has dissolved.

Bring to boil and boil to 116C (240F) on a sugar thermometer. Remove from heat. In a bowl, whisk egg whites until stiff. Pour hot syrup onto egg white, beating constantly. Continue beating as mixture cools. Use some frosting to sandwich cakes together; cover cake with the remainder. Decorate with walnut halves. Leave to set overnight.

Serves 8.

—— PINEAPPLE PASSION CAKE ——

175 g (6 oz) carrots, peeled and grated
85 g (3 oz/1 cup) walnuts
425 g (15 oz) can crushed pineapple
175 g (6 oz/1 cup) light soft brown sugar
3 eggs
300 g (10 oz/2½ cups) plain flour
1 teaspoon bicarbonate of soda
2 teaspoons baking powder
175 ml (6 fl oz/¾ cup) sunflower oil
FROSTING:
115 g (4 oz) cream cheese
55 g (2 oz/¼ cup) soft butter
175 g (6 oz/1 cup) icing sugar
few drops vanilla essence
TO DECORATE:
crystallised pineapple

Preheat oven to 180C (350F/Gas 4). Grease a
23 cm (9 in) loose-bottomed cake tin and line
base with non-stick paper. Stir carrot into a
bowl. Chop walnuts; add to carrots. Drain
pineapple and add to bowl with sugar and
eggs. Sift flour, bicarbonate of soda and
baking powder into bowl. Add sunflower oil
and beat thoroughly to make a smooth batter.
Pour into prepared tin. Bake in the oven for
50-60 minutes until well risen and a skewer
inserted into the centre comes out clean.

Transfer cake to a wire rack to cool. To make
frosting, beat together cream cheese, butter,
icing sugar and vanilla essence in a bowl until
smooth. Spread over cake. Decorate with
crystallised pineapple.

Serves 10-12.

—CHOC ORANGE RING CAKE—

2 small oranges
85 g (3 oz) plain (dark) chocolate
200 g (7 oz/1¾ cups) self-raising flour
1½ teaspoons baking powder
175 g (6 oz/¾ cup) soft margarine
175 g (6 oz/¾ cup) caster sugar
3 eggs, beaten
TO GLAZE:
225 g (8 oz/1½ cups) icing sugar
6 teaspoons orange juice
55 g (2 oz) plain (dark) chocolate

Preheat the oven to 160C (325F/Gas 3). Thoroughly grease an 850 ml (30 fl oz/3¾ cup) fluted or plain ring mould.

Cut skin and pith from oranges. Cut oranges into segments by cutting down between membranes. Chop segments into small pieces. Reserve as much juice as possible. Grate chocolate coarsely. Sift flour and baking powder into a bowl. Add margarine, sugar, eggs and any reserved orange juice. Beat thoroughly until mixture is smooth. Fold in chopped oranges and grated chocolate. Spoon mixture into prepared tin.

Bake in the oven for 40 minutes until well risen and golden brown. Leave in tin for 5 minutes, then transfer to a wire rack to cool completely. To make icing, sift icing sugar into a bowl and stir in enough orange juice to make a coating consistency. Using a spoon, drizzle icing over cake. Break chocolate into a bowl and melt over a pan of simmering water. Drizzle chocolate over cake. Leave to set.

Makes 8-10 slices.

—LEMON MOUSSE GÂTEAU—

CAKE:
3 eggs
130 g (4½ oz/½ cup plus 3 teaspoons) caster sugar
few drops vanilla essence
85 g (3 oz/¾ cup) plain flour
FILLING:
grated rind and juice 2 lemons
2 teaspoons powdered gelatine
3 eggs, separated
115 g (4 oz/½ cup) caster sugar
150 ml (5 fl oz/⅔ cup) double (thick) cream
TO DECORATE:
icing sugar
raspberries
lemon geranium or raspberry leaves, if available

Preheat oven to 180C (350F/Gas 4). Grease a 23 cm (9 in) spring-release tin and line with non-stick paper. To make cake, whisk eggs and caster sugar together in a bowl until very thick and light. Stir in vanilla essence, then sift flour over mixture and fold in gently. Spoon into prepared tin and bake in oven for 25 minutes until golden and the cake springs back when pressed. Turn onto a wire rack covered with sugared greaseproof paper. Peel off lining paper and leave to cool.

Slice the cake horizontally into 2 layers. Wash and dry cake tin and line base and sides with greaseproof paper. Place one half of cake in base of tin.

To make mousse filling, put juice of 1 lemon and 3 teaspoons water in a bowl. Sprinkle over gelatine, ensuring it is completely covered with liquid. Leave to stand for 10 minutes until spongy. In a bowl, whisk together egg yolks, sugar and lemon rind until thick and mousse-like. Gradually whisk in remaining lemon juice, keeping mixture as thick as possible.

Place bowl of gelatine over a pan of simmering water until gelatine has dissolved. Immediately whisk it into egg yolk mixture. In a bowl, whip cream until it just holds its shape. Fold cream into egg mixture. Whisk egg whites until stiff but not dry. Gently fold into mousse. Pour mixture into prepared tin. Level surface. Cover and chill for 45-60 minutes until lightly set. Place second layer of cake on top. Cover and chill overnight.

To serve, remove sides of tin and carefully peel away paper. Place a flat plate on top of cake and quickly invert cake. Ease off bottom of tin. Dust gâteau with sifted icing sugar and decorate with raspberries and geranium or raspberry leaves, if using.

Serves 8-10.

COFFEE CARAMEL CAKE

225 g (8 oz/2 cups) self-raising flour
175 g (6 oz/¾ cup) soft butter
175 g (6 oz/¾ cup) caster sugar
3 eggs, beaten
100 ml (3½ fl oz/⅓ cup) strong black coffee
ICING:
115 ml (4 fl oz/½ cup) creamy milk
130 g (4½ oz/½ cup plus 3 teaspoons) butter
9 teaspoons caster sugar
575 g (1¼ lb/3¾ cups) icing sugar
TO DECORATE:
chocolate coffee beans

Preheat oven to 180C (350F/Gas 4). Grease two 20 cm (8 in) sandwich tins; line bases with non-stick paper.

Sift flour 3 times and set aside. In a bowl, beat together butter and sugar until light and fluffy. Gradually beat in eggs. Fold in flour and coffee. Divide mixture between prepared tins and bake in oven for 30 minutes until risen and slightly shrinking from sides of tin. Cool in tins for 5 minutes, then transfer to wire racks to cool. To make icing, warm milk and butter in a saucepan.

In another heavy-based saucepan, heat caster sugar over a gentle heat until it dissolves and turns a golden caramel. Off the heat, stir in warm milk, taking care as it may splutter. Return to the heat and stir until caramel has dissolved. Remove from heat. Gradually stir in icing sugar, beating until icing is a smooth spreading consistency. Sandwich cakes together with some icing; spread remainder over top and sides. Decorate with chocolate coffee beans.

Serves 8-10.

—— TIA MARIA CHOUX RING ——

1 quantity Choux Pastry, see page 84
6 teaspoons plain flour
6 teaspoons cornflour
55 g (2 oz/¼ cup) caster sugar
300 ml (10 fl oz/1¼ cups) milk
3 egg yolks
150 ml (5 fl oz/⅔ cup) whipping cream
coffee essence
2 teaspoons Tia Maria
115 g (4 oz/¾ cup) icing sugar

Preheat oven to 220C (425F/Gas 7). Put pastry in a piping bag fitted with a 1 cm (½ in) plain nozzle.

Pipe a double 20 cm (8 in) ring onto a paper-lined baking sheet. Bake ring in the oven for 20 minutes. Lower the temperature to 180C (350F/Gas 4); bake for a further 10-15 minutes until golden brown and hollow. Split horizontally; cool on a wire rack. Sift flour and cornflour into a bowl. Stir in sugar and 2 tablespoons milk. Stir to form a thick paste. Whisk in egg yolks. In a saucepan, heat remaining milk to just below boiling point. Pour onto egg mixture, stirring constantly.

Strain mixture back into saucepan and cook gently, stirring constantly, until thickened. Cover closely with plastic wrap and leave until cold. In a bowl, stiffly whip cream and fold into custard. Stir in 2 teaspoons coffee essence and the Tia Maria. Sandwich choux rings together with coffee filling. In a bowl, mix together sifted icing sugar, few drops coffee essence and about 3 teaspoons water. Spoon over cake and leave to set.

Serves 8.

MAIDS OF HONOUR

1½ quantities Shortcrust Pastry, see page 89
115 g (4 oz) cottage cheese
55 g (2 oz/¼ cup) softened butter
55 g (2 oz/¼ cup) caster sugar
grated rind and juice ½ lemon
25 g (1 oz/¼ cup) ground almonds
½ teaspoon grated nutmeg
2 teaspoons brandy
55 g (2 oz/⅓ cup) currants
TO FINISH:
caster sugar, for sprinkling

Roll out pastry and use to line 12 tartlet tins. Chill for 30 minutes.

Preheat oven to 190C (375F/Gas 5). Sieve cottage cheese into a bowl. Add butter and beat until well blended. Add sugar, lemon rind and juice, ground almonds, nutmeg and brandy. Mix thoroughly. Stir in currants.

Spoon mixture into prepared pastry cases. Bake in the oven for 20-30 minutes until risen and golden brown. Sprinkle with caster sugar. Transfer to a wire rack to cool.

Makes 12.

PALMIERS

225 g (8 oz) puff pastry, thawed if frozen
55 g (2 oz/¼ cup) caster sugar
extra sugar, for rolling out
FILLING:
115 ml (4 fl oz/½ cup) double (thick) cream
4 teaspoons red jelly (such as redcurrant jelly)

Preheat oven to 220C (425F/Gas 7). On a surface dredged with caster sugar, roll out pastry to a 30 cm (12 in) square and sprinkle with half the sugar. Fold sides of pastry into the middle, sprinkle with half remaining sugar and fold sides into the middle again.

Sprinkle pastry with remaining sugar and fold in half down the middle. Press lightly. Cut pastry into 24 slices. Place slices, cut edge down, on dampened baking sheets. Press to flatten slightly. Bake in the oven for 10 minutes, or until crisp and a light golden brown. Turn over and bake for a further 2-3 minutes until second side is golden brown. Remove from baking sheets immediately and cool on wire racks.

In a bowl, whip cream until holding soft peaks. Spread a little jelly on 12 of the palmiers. Spread cream over jelly and top with remaining 12 palmiers.

Makes 12.

RASPBERRY ÉCLAIRS

CHOUX PASTRY:
55 g (2 oz/¼ cup) unsalted butter or margarine
70 g (2½ oz/⅓ cup) plain flour, sifted
2 eggs, beaten
FILLING:
175 ml (6 fl oz/¾ cup) double (thick) cream
3 teaspoons icing sugar
175 g (6 oz) raspberries
ICING:
115 g (4 oz/¾ cup) icing sugar, sifted
2 teaspoons lemon juice
pink food colouring (optional)

Preheat oven to 220C (425F/Gas 7). In a saucepan, melt butter or margarine, add 150 ml (5 fl oz/⅔ cup) water and bring to the boil. Add flour, all at once, and beat thoroughly until mixture leaves the side of the pan. Cool slightly, then vigorously beat in eggs, one at a time. Put mixture into a piping bag fitted with a plain 1 cm (½ in) nozzle and pipe twenty to twenty four 7.5 cm (3 in) lengths onto dampened baking sheets. Bake in the oven for 10 minutes. Reduce temperature to 190C (375F/Gas 5) and bake for 20 minutes until golden.

Slit the side of each éclair and leave on wire racks to cool. Make filling, whip cream and icing sugar in a bowl until thick, put in a piping bag fitted with a 0.3 cm (⅛ in) plain nozzle and pipe into each éclair. Put a few raspberries in each éclair. Make icing, mix icing sugar with lemon juice and enough water to make a smooth paste. Add pink colouring, if desired. Spread icing over éclairs and leave to set.

Makes 20-24.

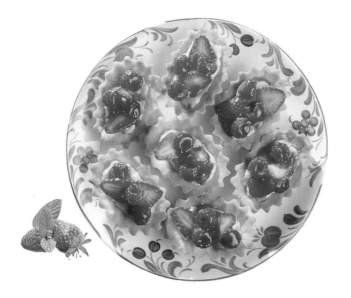

——SUMMER FRUIT TARTLETS——

PASTRY:
200 g (7 oz/1¾ cups) plain flour, sifted
55 g (2 oz/½ cup) ground almonds
85 g (3 oz/½ cup) icing sugar, sifted
115 g (4 oz/½ cup) butter
1 egg yolk
3 teaspoons milk
FILLING:
225 g (8 oz) cream cheese
caster sugar, to taste
350 g (12 oz) fresh summer fruits, such as red and
  blackcurrants, raspberries and wild strawberries
redcurrant jelly, heated, to glaze

In a bowl, mix together flour, ground almonds and icing sugar. Rub in butter until mixture resembles breadcrumbs. Add egg yolk and milk; work in with a palette knife, then with fingers, until dough binds together. Wrap dough in plastic wrap and chill for 30 minutes. Preheat the oven to 200C (400F/ Gas 6). On a floured surface, roll out pastry thinly and use to line 12 deep tartlet or individual brioche tins; prick bases.

Press a piece of foil into each tartlet, covering the edges. Bake in the oven for 10-15 minutes until light golden brown. Remove foil and bake for a further 2-3 minutes. Transfer to a wire rack to cool. To make filling, mix cream cheese and caster sugar together in a bowl. Put a spoonful of filling in each pastry case. Arrange fruit on top, brush with glaze and serve at once.

Makes 12.

MAPLE PECAN TARTS

PASTRY:
150 g (5 oz/1¼ cups) plain flour
85 g (3 oz/⅓ cup) butter
9 teaspoons icing sugar
1 egg yolk
1 teaspoon lemon juice
FILLING:
6 teaspoons maple syrup
150 ml (5 fl oz/⅔ cup) double (thick) cream
115 g (4 oz/½ cup) caster sugar
pinch cream of tartar
115 g (4 oz/1 cup) pecan nuts plus extra to decorate

To make pastry, sift flour into a bowl. Rub in butter until mixture resembles breadcrumbs.

Stir in icing sugar, egg yolk, lemon juice and about 1 teaspoon water to form a firm dough. Knead lightly. Chill for 30 minutes. Preheat oven to 200C (400F/Gas 6). On a floured surface, roll out pastry thinly and use to line 14 tartlet tins; prick bases. Press a piece of foil into each pastry shell. Bake in the oven for 10-15 minutes until light golden brown. Remove foil and bake for a further 2-3 minutes. Transfer to a wire rack to cool.

To make filling, mix half the maple syrup with half the cream. Put sugar and cream of tartar into a pan with 70 ml (2½ fl oz/⅓ cup) water. Heat gently until sugar dissolves. Bring to boil; boil until a light golden. Stir in syrup and cream mixture. Return to heat; cook to soft ball stage (116C/240F); forms a soft ball when dropped in cold water. Stir in remaining cream. Leave until warm. Brush syrup over edges of tarts. Put nuts in tarts. Spoon over toffee. Top each with a pecan.

Makes 14.

——— LEMON CUSTARD SLICES ———

225 g (8 oz) puff pastry, thawed if frozen
FILLING:
25 g (1 oz/3 tablespoons) cornflour
55 g (2 oz/¼ cup) caster sugar
150 ml (5 fl oz/⅔ cup) milk
juice 1 lemon
grated rind ½ lemon
1 egg yolk
115 ml (4 fl oz/½ cup) double (thick) cream
TO DECORATE:
85 g (3 oz/½ cup) icing sugar, sifted
2 kiwi fruit, peeled and sliced

Preheat oven to 230C (450F/Gas 8). On a floured surface, roll pastry out thinly to a rectangle 30 x 25 cm (12 x 10 in). With a sharp, floured knife, cut pastry into 8 rectangles. Prick all over with a fork. Place pastry slices on a dampened baking sheet. Bake in the oven for 10-15 minutes until well risen and golden brown. Transfer to a wire rack to cool. Split slices in half.

To make filling, smoothly blend cornflour with sugar and milk in a saucepan; boil, stirring, until mixture thickens. Stir in lemon juice and rind. Beat in egg yolk. Cover and leave to cool. Beat in cream. Mix icing sugar with about 6 teaspoons water to make a smooth paste. Spread over one side of 8 pastry slices. Leave to set. Spread custard over remaining pastry slices. Top with iced slices. Decorate with kiwi fruit.

Makes 8.

NUTTY FILO FINGERS

115 g (4 oz/1¼ cups) ground hazelnuts
55 g (2 oz/¼ cup) granulated sugar
3 teaspoons orange flower water
85 g (3 oz/⅓ cup) unsalted butter
6 large sheets filo pastry
TO FINISH:
caster sugar, for dusting

Preheat oven to 180C (350F/Gas 4). Grease 2 baking sheets. In a bowl, mix together ground hazelnuts, granulated sugar and orange flower water.

In a saucepan, melt butter. Cut each sheet of pastry into 4 rectangles. Pile on top of each other and cover with a tea-towel to prevent drying out. Working with one filo rectangle at a time, brush the pastry with melted butter.

Spread a teaspoon of filling along one short end. Fold long sides in, slightly over filling. Roll up from filling end. Place on one of the prepared baking sheets with seam underneath; brush with melted butter. Repeat with remaining pastry and filling. Bake in the oven for 20 minutes or until very lightly coloured. Transfer to wire racks to cool; sprinkle with caster sugar.

Makes 24.

FRANGIPANE TARTS

SHORTCRUST PASTRY:
115 g (4 oz/1 cup) plain flour
pinch of salt
55 g (2 oz/¼ cup) butter or margarine
FILLING:
6 teaspoons apricot jam
55 g (2 oz/¼ cup) butter
55 g (2 oz/¼ cup) caster sugar
1 egg
½ teaspoon almond essence
3 teaspoons plain flour, sifted
55 g (2 oz/½ cup) ground almonds
TOPPING:
25 g (1 oz/¼ cup) flaked almonds
6 teaspoons apricot jam

Preheat oven to 190C (375F/Gas 5). Sift flour and salt into a bowl. Rub in fat until mixture resembles breadcrumbs. Add 1-2 tablespoons water to bind mixture to a soft dough. On a floured surface, roll out pastry thinly and use to line 12 tartlet tins. Put a little apricot jam in the base of each pastry shell. To make filling, beat butter and sugar in a bowl until creamy. Mix egg and almond essence together; add to creamed mixture with flour and ground almonds. Mix well to form a smooth paste.

Spoon mixture into pastry cases. Arrange a few flaked almonds on top of each one. Bake in the oven for 15-20 minutes until golden. To make topping, heat jam with 2 teaspoons cold water in a saucepan. Bring to the boil; sieve and reheat. Brush over hot tarts. Transfer tarts to a wire rack to cool.

Makes 12.

——— ALMOND MACAROONS ———

2 egg whites
85 g (3 oz/¾ cup) ground almonds
115 g (4 oz/½ cup) caster sugar
2 teaspoons ground rice or cornflour
few drops almond essence
12 split, blanched almonds

Preheat oven to 180C (350F/Gas 4). Line 2 baking sheets with rice paper or non-stick paper. Reserve 2 teaspoons egg white. Put remaining egg white in a large bowl and whisk until standing in soft peaks.

Fold in ground almonds, caster sugar, ground rice and almond essence until mixture is smooth. Put 6 spoonfuls of mixture onto each baking sheet and flatten slightly. Place a split almond in the centre of each round. Brush lightly with reserved egg white.

Bake in the oven for 20 minutes until very lightly browned. Allow to cool on baking sheets. When cold, remove macaroons from baking sheets and tear away excess rice paper or all the non-stick paper from each one.

Makes 12.

LINZER HEARTS

115 g (4 oz/½ cup) butter
55 g (2 oz/¼ cup) caster sugar
1 egg, beaten
few drops almond essence
200 g (7 oz/1¾ cups) plain flour
25 g (1 oz/3 tablespoons) cornflour
½ teaspoon baking powder
FILLING:
6 tablespoons raspberry jam
TO FINISH:
icing sugar, for sifting

In a bowl, beat butter and sugar together until creamy. Gradually beat in egg, then beat in almond essence, to taste.

Sift flour, cornflour and baking powder into bowl and blend together with a spoon, then work by hand to form a soft dough. Chill for 30 minutes. Preheat oven to 180C (350F/Gas 4). Butter several baking sheets. Roll dough out on a floured surface to 0.3 cm (⅛ in) thick. Using a 5 cm (2 in) heart cutter, cut out heart shapes from dough. Using a smaller heart cutter, cut out hearts from the centre of 20 of the hearts. Re-knead and re-roll trimmings and cut out more shapes to make 40 in total, half with the centre cut out.

Bake in the oven for 15 minutes until very lightly browned. Remove from baking sheets to wire racks to cool. Dust biscuits with cutout centres with icing sugar. Spread whole hearts with raspberry jam and top with cutout biscuits.

Makes 20.

JUMBLES

150 g (5 oz/²/₃ cup) butter
150 g (5 oz/²/₃ cup) caster sugar
1 egg, beaten
225 g (8 oz/2 cups) plain flour
55 g (2 oz/½ cup) ground almonds
grated rind 1 lemon
GLAZE:
6 teaspoons clear honey
6 teaspoons demerara sugar

In a bowl, beat butter with caster sugar until creamy. Gradually beat in egg.

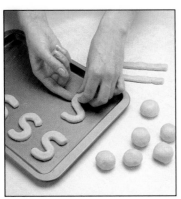

Sift flour onto creamed mixture; add ground almonds and lemon rind. Mix well to make a firm dough. Knead lightly, wrap in plastic wrap and chill for 30 minutes. Preheat oven to 180C (350F/Gas 4). Grease several baking sheets. Divide dough into 32 pieces. Roll each piece into a pencil thin strip 10 cm (4 in) long. Twist into an S shape and place on a baking sheet. Bake in the oven for 15 minutes, until very lightly browned.

To glaze, brush the warm jumbles with honey and sprinkle with demerara sugar. Return to the oven for 2 minutes. Allow to cool on baking sheets for a few minutes, then remove to wire racks to cool completely.

Makes 32.

─── GINGER-TOPPED FINGERS ───

BISCUIT BASE:
225 g (8 oz/2 cups) plain flour
1 teaspoon ground ginger
85 g (3 oz/⅓ cup) caster sugar
175 g (6 oz/¾ cup) butter
TOPPING:
3 teaspoons golden syrup
55 g (2 oz/¼ cup) butter
6 teaspoons icing sugar, sifted
1 teaspoon ground ginger

Preheat oven to 180C (350F/Gas 4). Butter a shallow 27.5 x 17.5 cm (11 x 7 in) oblong tin. Sift flour and ginger into a bowl; stir in sugar.

Rub in butter until mixture begins to stick together. Press mixture into prepared tin and smooth top with a palette knife. Bake in the oven for 40 minutes until biscuits are very lightly browned.

To make topping, put syrup and butter in a small pan. Heat gently until melted. Stir in icing sugar and ginger. Pour topping over base while both are still hot. Allow to cool slightly, then cut into fingers. Remove to wire racks to cool completely.

Makes 16.

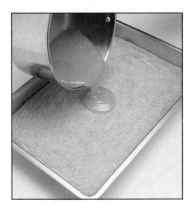

— SPICED APRICOT SQUARES —

225 g (8 oz/2 cups) plain flour
1 teaspoon mixed spice
115 g (4 oz/1¼ cups) ground almonds
1 egg, beaten
225 g (8 oz/1½ cups) caster sugar
175 g (6 oz/¾ cup) butter
115 g (4 oz/⅓ cup) apricot jam
TO FINISH:
icing sugar, for sifting

Sift flour and spice into a bowl. Add ground almonds, egg, sugar and butter. Beat well until thoroughly combined. Knead lightly. Wrap in plastic wrap and chill for at least 30 minutes.

Butter a shallow 27.5 x 17.5 cm (11 x 7 in) oblong tin. Press half the dough into tin. Spread apricot jam over dough. On a floured surface, lightly knead remaining dough. Roll out and cut into thin strips. Arrange the strips over the jam to form a close lattice pattern. Chill for 30 minutes. Preheat oven to 180C (350F/Gas 4).

Bake in the oven for 30-40 minutes until lightly browned. Leave the biscuits to cool in the tin, then sift icing sugar over the top. Cut into 24 squares or bars.

Makes 24.

——COFFEE WALNUT COOKIES——

225 g (8 oz/2 cups) plain flour, sifted
225 g (8 oz/1 cup) butter, softened
150 g (5 oz/1 cup) icing sugar, sifted
1 egg yolk
few drops vanilla essence
150 g (5 oz/1¼ cups) coarsely chopped walnuts
2 tablespoons medium ground fresh coffee
115 g (4 oz/1¼ cups) walnut pieces

Preheat oven to 180C (350F/Gas 4). Butter
several baking sheets.

Sift flour into a bowl, add butter, icing sugar,
egg yolk and vanilla essence. Mix well, then
mix in the chopped walnuts and the ground
coffee by hand.

Place heaped teaspoonfuls of mixture on
prepared baking sheets. Flatten slightly and
top each mound with a piece of walnut. Bake
in the oven for 12-15 minutes until just
starting to colour. Allow to cool on baking
sheets for a few minutes, then remove to wire
racks to cool completely.

Makes 28-30.

LEMON SHORTBREAD

115 g (4 oz/½ cup) butter
55 g (2 oz/¼ cup) caster sugar
150 g (5 oz/1¼ cups) plain flour
¼ teaspoon ground nutmeg
25 g (1 oz/2 tablespoons) ground rice or cornflour
grated rind 1 lemon
TO FINISH:
caster sugar and nutmeg, for sprinkling

In a bowl, beat butter with sugar until creamy. Sift flour and nutmeg into bowl, then add ground rice and lemon rind. Blend in with a spoon, then work by hand to form a soft dough.

Knead dough lightly on a floured surface until smooth. Roll out to a smooth round, about 15 cm (6 in) in diameter. Very lightly flour a 17.5 cm (7 in) shortbread mould. Place shortbread, smooth side down, in mould. Press out to fit mould exactly. Very carefully unmould shortbread onto a baking sheet. Refrigerate for 1 hour. (If you do not have a shortbread mould, shape dough into a neat round. Place on baking sheet, prick well with a fork, then pinch edge to decorate.)

Preheat oven to 160C (325F/Gas 3). Bake shortbread in the oven for 35-40 minutes until cooked through, but still pale in colour. Immediately shortbread is removed from the oven, sprinkle lightly with caster sugar and nutmeg. Allow to cool on baking sheet for about 20 minutes, then very carefully transfer to a wire rack to cool completely.

Makes 1.

FLORENTINES

55 g (2 oz/¼ cup) unsalted butter
85 ml (3 fl oz/⅓ cup) double (thick) cream
85g (3 oz/⅓ cup) caster sugar
finely grated rind 1 lemon
1 teaspoon lemon juice
55 g (2 oz/½ cup) plain flour, sifted
85 g (3 oz/½ cup) slivered blanched almonds
115 g (4 oz/¾ cup) chopped mixed candied citrus peel
55 g (2 oz/⅓ cup) chopped glacé cherries
25 g (1 oz/2 tablespoons) sultanas
25 g (1 oz/2 tablespoons) chopped angelica
TO FINISH:
85g (3 oz) plain (dark) chocolate, chopped
85 g (3 oz) white chocolate, chopped

Preheat oven to 180C (350F/Gas 4). Grease
several baking sheets. Line with non-stick
paper. Put butter, cream, sugar, lemon rind
and juice into a large saucepan and stir over a
moderate heat until melted. Remove from
heat and stir in flour, almonds, mixed peel,
cherries, sultanas and angelica. Drop teaspoonfuls of mixture onto baking sheets;
space well apart. Using a fork dipped in cold
water, flatten each round to a circle about
6 cm (2½ in) in diameter.

Bake in the oven for 10-12 minutes until
lightly browned around edges. Cool on
baking sheets for a few minutes, then remove
with a palette knife to wire racks to cool
completely. Melt plain (dark) and white
chocolate in bowls placed over pans of hot,
not boiling, water. Spread flat sides of half
the florentines with plain (dark) chocolate,
and the remainder with white chocolate.
Using a fork, mark chocolate into wavy lines.
Leave to set, chocolate uppermost.

Makes 28.

DOUBLE CHOCOLATE COOKIES

115 g (4 oz/½ cup) butter
55 g (2 oz/¼ cup) granulated sugar
55 g (2 oz/⅓ cup) soft brown sugar
1 egg, beaten
few drops vanilla essence
130 g (4½ oz/1 cup plus 6 teaspoons) plain flour
15 g (½ oz/2 tablespoons) cocoa
½ teaspoon bicarbonate of soda
150 g (5 oz) white chocolate chips

Preheat oven to 180C (350F/Gas 4). Butter several baking sheets.

In a bowl, beat butter with granulated and soft brown sugar until creamy. Gradually add egg and vanilla essence. Sift flour, cocoa and bicarbonate of soda into bowl. Mix well, then stir in chocolate chips.

Drop teaspoonfuls of mixture, well spaced out, onto prepared baking sheets. Bake in the oven for 10-12 minutes until firm. Allow to cool on baking sheets for a few minutes, then remove to wire racks to cool completely.

Makes about 48.

— ORANGE-GLAZED SHORTIES —

225 g (8 oz/1 cup) butter
55 g (2 oz/⅓ cup) icing sugar, sifted
grated rind 1 orange
½ teaspoon ground coriander
225 g (8 oz/2 cups) plain flour
GLAZE:
2 teaspoons apricot jam, heated and sieved
9 teaspoons icing sugar, sifted
3 teaspoons orange juice

Preheat oven to 180C (350F/Gas 4). Butter several baking sheets and dust them lightly with flour.

In a bowl, beat butter with icing sugar until very light and creamy. Stir in the orange rind. Sift the coriander and flour into a bowl, then work into creamy mixture with a wooden spoon to form a soft dough. Put mixture into a piping bag fitted with a large star nozzle. Pipe rings of mixture onto prepared baking sheets. Chill for 30 minutes, then bake in the oven for 20 minutes until biscuits are very lightly browned.

To glaze, brush each shortie with a little heated and sieved apricot jam. In a small bowl, mix together the icing sugar and orange juice and brush over biscuits. Return shorties to the oven for 2-3 minutes until glaze is set. Cool on baking sheets for a few minutes, then transfer to wire racks to cool.

Makes 25-28.

─── CHERRY NUT SHORTCAKE ───

SHORTCAKE:
175 g (6 oz/1½ cups) plain flour
55 g (2 oz/¼ cup) caster sugar
115 g (4 oz/½ cup) butter
TOPPING:
55 g (2 oz) coarsely chopped Brazil nuts
85 g (3 oz/½ cup) quartered glacé cherries
9 teaspoons thick honey

Preheat oven to 160C (325F/Gas 3). Grease an 17.5 cm (7 in) loose-bottomed flan tin.

Sift flour into a bowl. Add sugar and rub in butter until mixture begins to stick together. Press mixture into prepared tin. Smooth top with a palette knife. Bake in the oven for 35 minutes until very lightly browned. Cool shortcake in tin.

To make topping, put nuts, cherries and honey in a small saucepan. Bring to the boil and simmer gently for 2 minutes until sticky. Spread mixture evenly over shortcake. Leave to cool. When topping is set, cut shortcake into 8 wedges.

Makes 8.

CHOCOLATE CHEQUERBOARDS

175 g (6 oz/¾ cup) butter
175 g (6 oz/¾ cup) caster sugar
few drops vanilla essence
2 eggs
505 g (1 lb 2 oz/4½ cups) plain flour
2 teaspoons baking powder
1 teaspoon milk
6 teaspoons cocoa

Grease several baking sheets. Divide butter and sugar equally between 2 bowls.

To make vanilla dough, beat one half of butter and sugar until light and fluffy. Beat in vanilla essence and 1 egg. Sift half flour and 1 teaspoon baking powder into bowl. Blend in with spoon, then work by hand to form a smooth dough. Make chocolate dough in same way with remaining butter, sugar and egg, adding milk and sifting cocoa in with remaining flour and baking powder. Divide each portion of dough into 4 equal pieces.

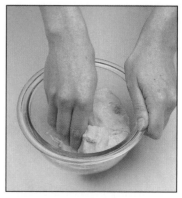

On a floured surface roll each piece into a rope 30 cm (12 in) long. Place a chocolate rope next to a vanilla one. Place a chocolate one on top of the vanilla one and a vanilla one on top of the chocolate. Press firmly together to form a square. Wrap in plastic wrap. Repeat with remaining dough. Chill for 1 hour. Preheat oven to 180C (350 F/Gas 4). Cut dough into 48 slices and place on baking sheets. Bake for 20 minutes until lightly browned.

Makes 48.

LEMON CURD

4 lemons
350 g (12 oz/1¾ cups) caster sugar
115 g (4 oz/½ cup) butter
4 eggs

Finely grate rind from all 4 lemons into a heatproof bowl. Squeeze lemons and pour juice into the bowl. Stir in sugar. Cut butter into small pieces and add to other ingredients in bowl.

Set bowl over a saucepan one-quarter filled with simmering water, until butter has melted and sugar dissolved. In a bowl, break up eggs with a fork and strain into lemon and butter mixture.

Cook gently, stirring frequently, for 10-15 minutes until mixture is thick and creamy. Pour into clean warm jars and seal while hot. Keep in the refrigerator.

Makes about 700 g (1½ lb).

Variations: For Lime Curd, use limes instead of lemons.

For Lemon & Elderflower Curd, add 2 handfuls of elderflowers, well shaken and flowers removed from stems, after adding the butter to the bowl.

——— APPLE BUTTER ———

1.2 litres (40 fl oz/5 cups) dry cider
1 kg (2.2 lb) dessert apples
450 g (1 lb) cooking apples
granulated sugar
grated rind and juice ½ orange
grated rind and juice ½ lemon
½ teaspoon ground cinnamon
½ teaspoon ground cloves

Put cider in a large saucepan. Boil rapidly until reduced by one-third. Peel, core and slice apples and add to pan.

If necessary, add sufficient water to just cover apples. Half-cover the pan and simmer gently until apples are very soft and pulpy and well reduced. Stir occasionally and crush pulp down in the pan as it cooks. Measure pulp and process to a purée if it is lumpy. Return to saucepan. Add 300 g (10 oz/1¼ cups) sugar for every 550 ml (20 fl oz/2½ cups) of apple pulp. Stir in the orange and lemon rind and juice and cinnamon and cloves.

Cook gently until sugar has dissolved. Simmer, stirring frequently, until most moisture has been driven off. The mixture is ready when a spoon drawn across the surface will leave an impression. Pot in clean, warm jars and store in the refrigerator. Once a jar is opened the apple butter should be consumed within 3-4 days.

Makes 4 or 5 small jars.

—CUMBERLAND RUM BUTTER—

115 g (4 oz/½ cup) butter, at room temperature
225 g (8 oz/1½ cups) soft dark brown sugar
¼ teaspoon ground cinnamon
6 teaspoons dark rum
TO SERVE:
hot toast, muffins or crumpets

Put butter into a bowl and beat until soft. Gradually beat in sugar.

Gradually beat in the cinnamon and rum. Pile mixture into a small dish. Cover and leave in a cool place until firm. Serve with hot toast, muffins or crumpets.

Serves 6-8.

Variation: For Anchovy Butter, instead of sugar, cinnamon and rum, work 45 g (1½ oz) drained, canned anchovies into butter. Serve on toast.

ROSE PETAL JAM

225 g (8 oz) red, fragrant rose petals
450 g (1 lb/2 cups) granulated sugar
juice of 2 lemons

Cut off white area from base of each petal.
Put petals in a bowl and sprinkle with enough
of the sugar to cover them. Leave overnight.

In a saucepan, put remaining sugar, 1 litre
(35 fl oz/4½ cups) water and the lemon juice.
Heat gently until sugar has dissolved. Stir in
rose petals and simmer for 20 minutes. Bring
to the boil and boil for 5 minutes until
mixture thickens.

Pour jam into clean, warm jars. Cover and
label. Store in a cool place.

Makes about 450 g (1 lb).

ICED ROSE TEA

45 g (1½ oz) Ceylon breakfast tea
1 litre (35 fl oz/4½ cups) lukewarm water
sugar, to taste
few drops rosewater, to taste
12 ice cubes
6 sprigs of mint
fresh rose petals

Put tea in a bowl, pour over warm water and leave to stand overnight.

Strain tea into a large jug. Stir in sugar and rosewater to taste and add ice cubes. Place a sprig of mint and a few rose petals in each of 6 glasses and pour the tea on top.

Serves 6.

Variations: For Vanilla Iced Tea, omit rosewater. Put a vanilla pod in the bowl with tea to soak overnight. Remove it before serving.

For Mint Tea, omit the rosewater and rose petals. Put a sprig of mint in the bowl with tea to soak overnight. Remove it before serving. Place a small sprig of fresh mint in each glass.

SPICED TEA

small piece fresh root ginger, peeled
4 whole cloves
2.5 cm (1 in) stick cinnamon
25 g (1 oz) Ceylon tea
55 g (2 oz/¼ cup) sugar
70 ml (2½ fl oz/⅓ cup) orange juice
juice of ½ lemon
TO DECORATE:
4-6 cinnamon sticks

Bruise ginger and put in a saucepan with cloves and cinnamon. Add 1 litre (35 fl oz/ 4½ cups) cold water and bring to the boil.

Put the tea in a bowl, pour on the spiced water and leave to infuse for 5 minutes. Add sugar and stir until dissolved, then stir in orange and lemon juice.

Reheat before serving, but do not allow to simmer or boil. Strain spiced tea into heatproof glasses. Serve with a cinnamon stick in each glass.

Serves 4-6.

Note: This drink is also delicious served chilled.

Variation: To make Party Punch, add extra sugar, to taste, then just before serving, add 300 ml (10 fl oz/1¼ cups) rum.

TENNIS CUP

225 g (8 oz/1 cup) granulated sugar
1 lemon
2 oranges
2 bottles red or white wine
550 ml (20 fl oz/2½ cups) soda water
TO DECORATE:
thin slices of cucumber and orange
borage flowers or violets, if available

Put sugar in a saucepan with 150 ml (5 fl oz/
⅔ cup) cold water. Heat gently until sugar
has dissolved. Bring to the boil and boil until
syrup reaches 105C (220F).

With a potato peeler, thinly pare rind from
lemon and oranges. Add to syrup and simmer
gently for 10 minutes. Set aside until
completely cold.

Squeeze juice from lemon and oranges and
strain into syrup, then pour in the wine and
chill. Just before serving, add soda water.
Pour into glasses. Decorate with slices of
cucumber and orange and sprigs of borage
or violets.

Makes about 2 litres (70 fl oz/9 cups).

SUMMER TEA CUP

1 Lapsang Souchon tea bag
550 ml (20 fl oz/2½ cups) boiling water
4 teaspoons soft brown sugar
300 ml (10 fl oz/1¼ cups) pineapple juice
70 ml (2½ fl oz/⅓ cup) white rum
550 ml (20 fl oz/2½ cups) ginger ale
ice cubes
TO DECORATE:
pieces fresh pineapple

Place tea bag in a bowl and pour over the boiling water.

Leave tea to infuse for 5 minutes, then remove tea bag. Stir in brown sugar and leave until cold. Stir the pineapple juice and rum into the cold tea.

Just before serving, pour ginger ale into tea. Add ice cubes. Place a few pieces of pineapple in each glass and pour in the chilled tea.

Makes about 1.5 litres (52 fl oz/6¾ cups).

—OLD-FASHIONED LEMONADE—

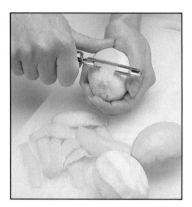

3 lemons
115 g (4 oz/½ cup) sugar
TO FINISH:
ice
sprigs of mint
lemon slices

Using a potato peeler, thinly pare the rind from the lemons and put in a bowl or large jug with sugar. Squeeze juice from lemons into a bowl and set aside.

Boil 850 ml (30 fl oz/3¼ cups) cold water and pour over lemon rind and sugar. Stir to dissolve sugar and leave until completely cool. Add lemon juice and strain into a jug. Chill well. Serve in ice-filled tumblers, decorated with mint and lemon slices.

Serves 6.

Variations: To make Pink Lemonade, add just enough pink grenadine syrup to each glass to give lemonade a pale pink colour. Omit the mint and lemon slices and decorate each glass with a cherry.

To make Orangeade, use 3 oranges and 1 lemon instead of 3 lemons. Omit the mint and lemon slices and decorate the glasses with orange slices.

—GRAPEFRUIT BARLEY WATER—

55 g (2 oz) pearl barley
55 g (2 oz/¼ cup) sugar
2 pink grapefruit
TO DECORATE:
mint leaves

Put barley into a saucepan. Just cover with cold water and bring to the boil. Tip barley into a colander and rinse thoroughly under cold running water.

Return barley to the saucepan, add 550 ml (20 fl oz/2½ cups) cold water and bring to the boil again. Cover and simmer for 1 hour. Strain liquid into a jug, stir in the sugar and leave until completely cold.

Squeeze juice from grapefruit and add to cooled barley water. Chill well. Serve decorated with mint leaves.

Makes about 550 ml (20 fl oz/2½ cups).

Variation: To make Lemon Barley Water, use 2 lemons instead of grapefruit.

Clockwise from top:

SALMON PINWHEELS
page 19

TURKEY TRIANGLES
page 17

AVOCADO & BACON SANDWICHES
page 15

SPICY CHICKEN SANDWICHES
page 16

Clockwise from top right:

SMOKED SALMON CROÛTES
page 27

SALAMI PUFFS
page 22

MINI QUICHES
page 30

CHEESE STRAWS
page 32

CRAB & GINGER TRIANGLES
page 25

DEVILLED HAM TOASTS
page 23

PARMESAN BEIGNETS
page 28

Centre:
SCOTCH EGGS
page 33

Clockwise from top left:

CRANBERRY BRAZIL LOAF
page 43

BRAMBLE MUFFINS
page 37

CRUMPETS
page 48

CHEESE & CHIVE PLAIT
page 45

WELSH CAKES
page 38

APPLE SCONE ROUND
page 36

CARAWAY KUGELHOPF
page 42

Centre:

LEMON & CURRANT BRIOCHES
page 47

CHELSEA BUNS
page 46

Clockwise from top right:

LEMON CRUNCH CAKE
page 50

COCONUT & CHERRY CAKE
page 53

DUNDEE CAKE
page 54

GINGER CAKE
page 51

APPLE STREUSEL CAKE
page 55

TOFFEE DATE CAKE
page 58

PEACH & ORANGE CAKE
page 59

Centre:

CHOCOLATE MARBLE CAKE
page 57

Clockwise from top:

BLACKCURRANT WHIRLS
page 60

QUEEN CAKES
page 68

STRAWBERRY-ROSE MERINGUES
page 61

LEMON BUTTERFLY CAKES
page 69

HONEY MADELEINES
page 62

CHOCOLATE BROWNIES
page 63

SPONGE DROPS
page 66

GINGER BRANDY SNAPS
page 67

Clockwise from top right:

FROSTED WALNUT CAKE
page 75

SUMMER SPONGE CAKE
page 70

DOUBLE CHOCOLATE GÂTEAU
page 72

PINEAPPLE PASSION CAKE
page 76

LEMON MOUSSE GÂTEAU
page 78

COFFEE CARAMEL CAKE
page 80

Centre:

CHOC ORANGE RING CAKE
page 77

Clockwise from top:

PALMIERS
page 83

SUMMER FRUIT TARTLETS
page 85

MAPLE PECAN TARTS
page 86

NUTTY FILO FINGERS
page 88

FRANGIPANE TARTS
page 89

MAIDS OF HONOUR
page 82

Clockwise from top:

JUMBLES
page 92

ORANGE-GLAZED SHORTIES
page 99

SPICED APRICOT SQUARES
page 94

LINZER HEARTS
page 91

COFFEE WALNUT COOKIES
page 95

CHERRY NUT SHORTCAKE
page 100

ALMOND MACAROONS
page 90

INDEX

The Half-Birthday Party

by Charlotte Pomerantz

illustrated by DyAnne DiSalvo-Ryan

Clarion Books

TICKNOR & FIELDS: A HOUGHTON MIFFLIN COMPANY

New York

Clarion Books
Ticknor & Fields, a Houghton Mifflin Company

Library of Congress Cataloging in Publication Data
Pomerantz, Charlotte.
The half-birthday party.
Summary: Daniel gives his six-month-old sister a
half-birthday party, to which each guest is asked to
bring half a present.
[1. Parties—Fiction.   2. Birthdays—Fiction]
I. DiSalvo-Ryan, DyAnne, ill.   II. Title.
PZ7.P77Hal   1984   [E]   84-4963
ISBN 0-89919-273-4

Printed in the U.S.A.
Y 10 9 8 7 6 5 4 3 2 1

for John A. Crocco, M.D.
integer vitae scelerisque purus

—C.P.

To my whole family

—D.D.R.

One day, when Daniel's sister Katie
was six months old,
she stood for the first time.
She took hold of a table leg
and pulled herself up.
"Daddy, Mommy, come quick," said Daniel.
"Katie is standing."

That evening, Daniel decided
to give Katie a half-birthday party.
He sent an invitation to Lily,
his friend across the hall.
And one to Grandma and Mr. Bangs,
who always came to parties with her.

The invitation read:

My sister Katie is six months old.
Please come to her half-birthday party
on Sunday afternoon at 3 o'clock. And
bring half a present.

Daniel

P.S. You have to tell a whole story
about the half present.

The day of the party,
Daniel woke up early.
Katie was asleep.
He blew up some balloons
and tied them to her crib.
He strung party streamers
from one end of the room
to the other.
Katie woke up and started to cry.

Daniel changed her diaper
and put her back in the crib.
Katie cried harder.
"Sorry, Katie," said Daniel.
"I can't pick you up. I'm busy."
Mother and Father came in.
They admired the balloons
and streamers.
Mother picked up Katie.

Father fixed breakfast.
"Have something to eat," he said.
"Not now, Daddy. I'm busy."

Daniel found a large sheet of
brown wrapping paper and wrote,
HAPPY HAF BIRTHDAY, KATIE.
"That's good," said Mother.
"But there's an L in HALF.
It goes between the A and the F."

Daniel put in the L and taped
the sign across the television screen.
Then he made a pitcher of lemonade.

"The cake!" cried Daniel.
"We forgot the birthday cake."
Mother smiled. "I didn't forget,"
she said. "Grandma is bringing it."

By three o'clock,
everyone had arrived with a gift.
"Look at Katie," said Grandma.
"She's sitting up."

"That's nothing," said Daniel.
"Watch this."
Daniel lifted Katie out of the crib
and put her down near the table.
Katie grabbed the table leg
and pulled herself up
to a standing position.
"She's a smart little pollywiggle,"
said Mr. Bangs.

Lily tapped a balloon.
"This is fun," she said.
"I've never been to a
half-birthday party before.
I can't wait for my turn."
She looked at Daniel.
"You should be the first to give
Katie a present and tell a story."

Daniel gulped. Oh, no!
He had been so busy getting ready
for the party that he had
forgotten Katie's present!
His heart was thumping.
"You go first," he said coolly.

Lily's Story

My dog Louie likes bedroom slippers
more than dog food.
So when I bought new slippers,
I hid them.
But Louie found them.

When I came home from school,
he was chomping on one.
I grabbed it. But it was so torn
and soggy that I threw it
back at him.
"Bad dog," I yelled.
"What can I do with one slipper!"

Then I got the invitation to
Katie's half birthday party.

Lily unwrapped her present
and went over to Katie.
"My half present is a
half pair of slippers," she said.
"That's one slipper.
Happy half-birthday, Katie."
Katie reached out and squeezed the slipper.
Then she put it in her mouth.
Lily hugged her.
"You're as bad as my dog Louie," she said.
She turned to Daniel.
"Thanks for letting me go first.
Now it's your turn."

Daniel felt hot and sweaty.
He still hadn't thought of a present.
"I'll go later," he said.
Mr. Bangs spoke up.
"Let your mother go next,"
he said. "I see she is
holding something very tiny.
And they say that the best things
come in small packages."
He chuckled. "That's a quote," he said.
"What's a quote?" asked Lily.
"When somebody else said it first,"
said Grandma.

Mother's Story

It happened a long time ago.
I was working in a shoe factory
and on my way home from work,
I stopped at a fruit and vegetable stand.
I was looking through the peaches
when I heard a tiny thud.
I reached up to check my gold earrings.
Sure enough, one had fallen off.
A young man came up to me.
"Please do not handle
the fruit," he said.
"But one of my gold earrings
fell into the peaches," I said.
"Oh dear," he said.
"I'll help you look."

We looked and looked.
The earring wasn't in the peaches.
"Let's try the bananas," he said.
"No," I said. "I didn't look
at the bananas. They're not ripe."
"The tomatoes are nice," he said.
"I have enough tomatoes," I said.
"How about some turnips?"
I made a face. "Ugh,
I don't like turnips."
"They are good in a stew," he said.
"I make a delicious turnip stew."
I looked him straight in the eye.
"Are you inviting me for dinner?"
"Yes, I am," he said.

"Did you ever find the lost earring?"
asked Daniel.
"No," said Mother. "But it was
the first time I met Father.
And it was the last time I ate
turnip stew."
She unwrapped the tiny gift.
"My half present is one gold earring.
But I can't give it to you, Katie,
till you're grown.
You might swallow it."
She gathered Katie into her arms.
"Happy half-birthday," she said.

Everyone liked the story,
especially Daniel's father.
Daniel stared out the window.
He was beginning to get an idea.
If only it were later
in the evening...

Suddenly the lights went out.
Mr. Bangs walked in,
carrying half a birthday cake.
It was lit by half a candle.
They all sang:

Happy half-birthday to you,
Happy half-birthday to you,
Happy half-birthday, dear Katie,
Happy half-birthday to you.

When the lights were turned on,
everyone could see the writing
on the cake.

"HAPPY HA?" said Daniel.
"What does that mean?"
Mr. Bangs shrugged.
"Don't ask me," he said.
"I just did what your
Grandmother told me to do.
Maybe she can explain."
"Of course, I can," said Grandma.

Grandma's Story

When we opened Daniel's invitation,
Mr. Bangs said that he would bake
a birthday cake.
I said, "No, dear. You have to bake
half a cake. And be sure and write
HAPPY HA on the top."
Mr. Bangs grumbled, but he did
what I asked him to do.

Grandma put down her present
and unwrapped it carefully.
It was also half a cake.
On top was written:

"I still don't get it," said Daniel.
Grandma placed her half
next to the other half.
Together, the two halves
looked like this:

"Wow," said Daniel. "That's neat."
His father was in a corner,
scribbling something.
Everyone else was eating cake
and drinking lemonade.

Daniel stepped out on
the fire escape.
He looked around him
at the lights of the city,
and up at the evening sky.
The brightest star
seemed to be winking at him.
"Wish me luck," he said,
and winked back.
He took a deep breath
and stepped inside.

Father was holding
a piece of paper.
"I wrote a poem for Katie," he said.

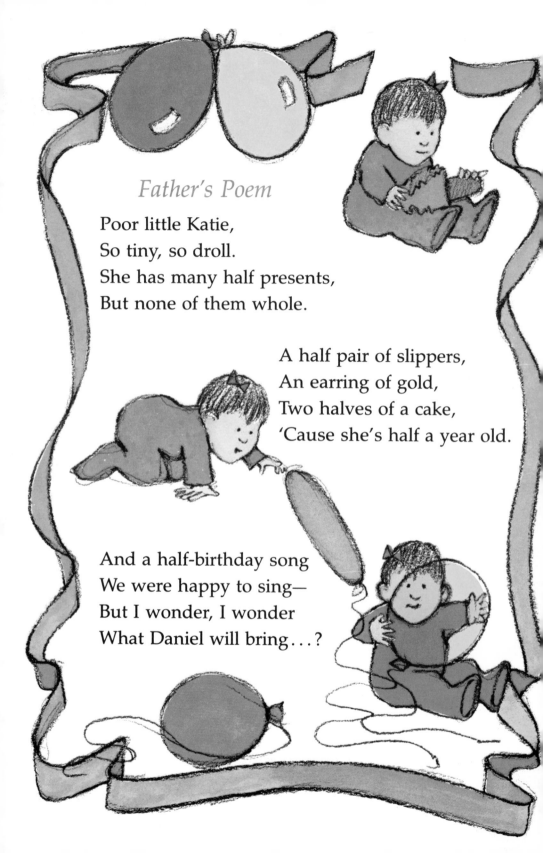

Father's Poem

Poor little Katie,
So tiny, so droll.
She has many half presents,
But none of them whole.

A half pair of slippers,
An earring of gold,
Two halves of a cake,
'Cause she's half a year old.

And a half-birthday song
We were happy to sing—
But I wonder, I wonder
What Daniel will bring...?

Grandma danced around, chanting,
"I'll bet you that Daniel
brought the *best* thing!"

"Probably," said Mr. Bangs.
"They say that the best things
come last."
"That's another quote," said Grandma.
Lily looked puzzled.
"I thought Mr. Bangs said that
the best things come in small packages."
"Mr. Bangs knows a lot of quotes,"
said Grandma.

Daniel sensed that everyone
was looking at him.
"Please come out on the fire escape,"
he said. "Katie, too."

"What do you see?" asked Daniel.
"I see cars and street lamps,"
said Father.
"I see tall buildings
and water towers,"
said Mother.

"I see a fish bowl on a
window sill," said Mr. Bangs.
Grandma put her arms
around Mr. Bangs. "I see
millions and millions
of stars," she said.
"Keep looking," said Daniel.

They looked and looked.
Up and down and around.
Then, all at once, they saw it,
Pale and lovely in the dusky sky.
The moon.
Only it wasn't a whole moon.
It was a half moon.

"Oo," said Lily. "Now I know."
Daniel took Katie from Father.

Daniel's Story

Once upon a time,
a boy gave his sister
a half-birthday party.
Everyone who came brought
beautiful presents.
But the boy had to wait
a long time to give his present.
At last, when it got dark,
he gave his sister
a half moon.

They all looked at Katie.
She was asleep in Daniel's arms.
The moonlight lit up her sleeping face.
"Daniel," his Mother whispered,
"is it true that you knew all
along that you would give Katie
a half-moon?"
A little smile crossed Daniel's face.
"It's half true," he said.